Pushkin

Pushkin
POET AND LOVER

LYDIA LAMBERT

TRANSLATED FROM THE FRENCH BY

WILLARD R. TRASK

DOUBLEDAY & CO., INC., GARDEN CITY, N. Y., 1946

Contents

The Moor Of Peter The Great

THE MANOR HOUSE OF MIK-hailovskoe was long and low, built with crossed timbers like a peasant's house; today its windows, with their panes of a greenish glass full of warts and bubbles, stood wide open. All winter the household had lived turned in upon themselves, with every opening stuffed up for fear of the deadly drafts that crept along the floors, coming through the badly fitting doors. But a short and violent spring had been followed in only a few days by summer, and overnight there was new grass where yesterday there had still been snow.

The master of Mikhailovskoe was old and black. The villagers feared him because of his great age, because of the color of his skin, because of his name, too, which was not a Christian name: it was Hannibal. But also because he would as soon have his servants give you fifty lashes as not —and after that there was nothing to do with you but to pick you up in a sheet.

Two footmen, tall, strong fellows in rags, whose status as house serfs did not prevent them from going barefoot and blowing their noses on their shirttails, were just in the act of leading their old black master down the entrance stairs of his wooden château. He could feel their big hard hands under his armpits as they carefully helped him down the steps that led to the garden.

He signed to them to seat him on a bench in the sunlight. The sun—that was the thing; it warmed the blood and sent it circulating through old, stiff limbs. He closed his eyes, folded both hands on the knob of his cane, and rested his chin on them in the attitude of the old. With his short, full-skirted coat (long, close-fitting coats were now in style) and the scant "cadogan" of gray hair that hung over the nape of his wrinkled neck like something out of Grandmother's day, he looked like an image of the past. Only the imperceptible nodding of his head showed that he was alive.

But deep in the age-shriveled body life flickered, tenacious and frail. He was alive because he could remember. From the depths of his mind his memories poured up, jostling, innumerable; and the oldest were the clearest.

He was said to be a hundred, the old black *barin* of Mikhailovskoe. He himself did not know exactly how old he was. Eighty-five? Ninety? Czar Peter was dead; Catherine was dead; Elisabeth, who had played with him as if he had been a doll, was dead. He alone remained, like a rock resisting the rising tide of eternity.

At the beginning of the century which was passing out in the disorder of these present days he, too, had been a page, a serf, a servant like the two who had brought him out there. And now he was a barin, a gentleman whose name appeared in the register of the Russian nobility.

And he had founded a family. From time to time his sons and daughters (he had had eighteen or nineteen children; he did not remember which) came to visit him, to celebrate a wedding or a birth. Some of them had died. He no longer remembered their faces; at times he confused their names. His sons already had white hair, like himself.

The chance that had made a poor Negro boy the master and the founder of a house of Russian gentlemen did not astonish him. Had he not royal blood in his veins? Was he not as much a nobleman as the proudest descendant of Rurik? Already, in the days when Russia was still being overrun by the Scythians, his ancestor Hannibal, whose name he had chosen to bear, was making Rome tremble.

Across a century of adventure his thoughts turned back to his native land, to Ethiopia and his father's rustic palace. The old *raz* was the ruler of three cities, of which one—Lagan (or Lagon), on the river Mareb—was built of stone. It was there that he had spent his childhood, in the shade of palms as high as cathedrals, on the bank of a river where pink ibises stood on one leg. His mother was the youngest of the raz's thirty wives, and he had nineteen brothers.

One day the palace was sacked, the palm grove burned to the ground, and Lagan was overrun by the Grand Turk's Janizaries. The razes were the Sultan's vassals and paid him tribute. When the Sultan thought he had not received his due in gold pieces and raw ivory and coffee and buckwheat, the Janizaries swept down on the country, pillaged, burned, decimated, then withdrew, carrying off the prettiest girls and the younger sons of the Ethiopian princes into slavery and leaving ruins where there had been cities.

It was in this fashion that he had been carried off by the invaders. His last picture of his native Africa was the sight of his mother swimming out after the boat that bore away her son.

Hannibal half opened his eyes. Around him lay the Russian countryside, stretching out flat and green under a pallid sky. The lake, with its cold blue depths, splashed softly among reeds. A cuckoo called its soft, persistent notes. He closed his eyes again. Now he could see Constantinople, with the Bosporus rippled like silk and full of refuse, with its alleys, its smells, and the grilled harem of the Grand Turk. It was there that the Turkish galleys had left him one evening, thin and haggard, but alive. For a year he had been the plaything of two hundred bored sultanas. They had given him the name of Ibrahim, which he had borne for almost a century.

He could see the harem on the night of his escape; he could still smell its sweetish odor of sweat and fat women, the odor of the seraglio.

After that it was Moscow, with the gilded domes of its churches, its mud, its impaled *streltzi*—Moscow, barely pacified, growling at Czar Peter, the headstrong, restless, fantastic young sovereign who dressed like a German, smoked a pipe, and shook hands with foreign merchants. Where, alas, were the days when Russian czars never let themselves be seen, except swathed like icons in cloaks that were stiff with gold and jewels and surrounded by an etiquette that had not changed since the days of the Byzantine emperors? To address them you must kneel with your forehead in the dust, and they never left their white and gilded Kremlin. But Peter could hardly wait to be crowned before he was off to travel in foreign countries. Even so— if only he had traveled with the dignity and splendor that became the heir to the emperors of Byzantium! But no, the Czar of All the Russias crossed Germany, Holland, France, and England on horseback and on foot, like a boor, stopping at inns, going into shops, taverns, hospitals. In Haarlem he had hired out as a carpenter's apprentice in a Dutch ship-builder's yard. And when he returned to Russia with a horde of foreign sailors, artisans, apothecaries, architects, and engineers, followed by coaches full of books, instruments, false teeth, wigs, harquebuses, and mounted skeletons, Holy Russia, living blessedly on her stoves, with her fleas and her cant, her knouts and her icons, believed that the reign of Antichrist had begun. The Czar himself cut off long beards and luxuriant robes and did not disdain at times to hang the recalcitrant with his own august hands. The *boyars* were ashamed of their naked faces and the wigs made of human hair that hung down to their navels. And if the King of France cured scrofula, the Czar pulled teeth —so that the subjects of the Autocrat of All the Russias had nothing for which to envy those of His Most Christian Majesty. . . .

When the Czar's own son sided with the malcontents he had him thrown into prison. Fortunately the Czarevitch, whose constitution was frail, died of fear and privation, thereby sparing his father the disgrace of publicly executing a descendant of the Byzantine emperors.

The times had indeed changed. Now boyars' sons wore malines lace and spoke French. The Empress Catherine had corresponded with Monsieur de Voltaire. And he, Hannibal, was the creation of the man who had effected this prodigious transformation—his work, like the new Russia. . . . The great Czar had been dead for sixty years, but he, Hannibal, was still called the Moor of Peter the Great.

He had been brought to Moscow with his companions— other Negro boys stolen in Constantinople or bought from the Janizaries—to make a show at the Russian court. He was given a red doublet embroidered with gold lace and a pair of buckled shoes. He served Czar Peter as page, aide-de-camp, and secretary. He slept in the Czar's bedroom. Often at night Peter would want to jot down an idea. He would wake the young African.

"Ibrahim!"

"Yes, sire."

"Bring the slate and a light."

Ibrahim would jump out of bed, take the slate from its hook, light a candle, and stand yawning, waiting for the Czar to finish writing.

Peter liked him. He often took him walking with him. People crossed themselves as the gigantic figure passed, wrapped in thought, walking heavily with a cane, huge, with his terrifying face and the scanty mustache whose hairs stood out stiffly like a cat's. Ibrahim trotted after him, wiping his face with his gold-laced sleeve.

One day Ibrahim stopped to relieve himself behind a bush. After a minute the Czar heard him calling:

"Sire, sire, there's a gut coming out of my belly!"

Peter went to him. "No, there isn't, stupid," he said. "That's not a gut, it's a tapeworm." And taking the boy around the waist, the Autocrat of All the Russias removed the parasite.

His memories rose like a tide.

Now it was not Moscow, with its overheated, low-ceilinged Kremlin, but Paris, paved and lighted, powdered, gallant, coquettish, rationalistic. . . . The charming, frivolous, courteous city of Law and the Duc de Richelieu.

Ibrahim had traveled with the Czar on his second journey through Europe: Ibrahim—or rather Abram Petrovich, the Czar's godson and aide-de-camp. Peter had had him baptized on the way, in Poland, in 1707. The Queen of Poland, King Augustus's wife, had been his godmother.

Peter left him in France to study the art of war so that he might become someone. Why not? He needed men. Abram had the fine and noble features of his race, a lively and curious mind. He would make a good engineer. So what did the color of his skin matter? And what a lesson for Peter's thick-skulled, fat-bottomed boyars to be under the orders of an "Arab"!

1714 . . . The War of the Spanish Succession. A young Negro engineer, a graduate of the Ecole de Vauban, fights in the French Army. Wounded in the head, he returns to Paris. Peter keeps calling him back to Russia, where he is short of men, of officers, of engineers. But is he to leave this laughing, civilized Paris, with its pretty women, its cafés, its shops—Paris, where fashion lives "the sweet days of a rose," where a grisette wears patches and panniers and walks as demurely as a great lady? Is he to go back to snowbound, barbarous Muscovy, when six years have made him French in mind and heart?

In answer to his letters the Czar receives long, embarrassed missives. . . . His studies are not quite finished, it will take another year or two, the roads are bad. Couldn't a few more crowns be sent him? Living is expensive in France, and besides, the professors must be paid, otherwise no more school. Signed: "Your unworthy slave, Abrashka."

Alas, the crowns became rarer and rarer, and Abram—godson of the Czar though he was—lived wretchedly enough. Peter was a miser; besides, communications were difficult. More than once the poor devil went to bed dinnerless in his unheated garret. Paris glittered under his window; he saw the luxurious life of its tax farmers and ballet girls. It was the women that troubled him most, the laughing, easily captured women of Paris. (Until then he had known only the fat, lazy women of the East.) These creatures, perched on heels as slim as needles, fascinated him with their grace. Unfortunately the poor Negro student had nothing with which to attract them. His figure was good, but his wretched clothes and cotton stockings were far from setting it off to advantage.

After six years no more excuses would serve: he must set out. Taking a regretful leave of the charming kingdom of France, the young engineer began his long return journey.

Moscow was no longer the capital of Russia. Peter had finally opened a window facing Europe. St. Petersburg was rising where, five years earlier, the Finnish marshes had stretched away in melancholy solitude. London, Rotterdam, and Hamburg were already sending to the new capital for flax and wood and furs. But the tireless builder was not long to enjoy his creation. In 1725 he died in the dockyards of his St. Petersburg.

Abram had been Peter's property, his slave, his creature. The Czar's death left him without a protector. He was soon in disgrace, and exile followed as a matter of course. The young Negro's adventurous destiny, which had decreed that he should be born in Africa and then had led him to Turkey, to Russia, and to France, now sent him to the uttermost limits of the world, to Siberia, on the Chinese frontier. Peter's daughter, the Empress Elisabeth, finally ended her old playmate's exile. From then on the stages of his life were marked by the increases in his wealth. Elisabeth had given him Mikhailovskoe with a thousand souls.

Catherine made him a gentleman and allowed him to take the name of Hannibal.

So now he had lived there for forty years with his wife, his children, his serfs—a patriarch, administering justice like his father, the Ethiopian raz. Half a century earlier he had asked Captain Dioper, a Greek, to give him his daughter in marriage. The girl looked on such a suitor with distaste, "because he is a Moor, and besides, not of our race." For Captain Dioper, who had ten daughters to marry off, Abram—black or not—was the Czar's godson. The marriage took place. A girl was born. She was white. The Moor had his wife whipped till the blood ran and sent her to prison in a fortress, where she was starved, for he refused to pay for her maintenance. But he was no more faithful than she. Without waiting for a divorce from his wife, he had married his mistress, Christine Scheberg.

The divorce dragged on for twenty years. Finally Eudoxia Dioper died, leaving him free to legitimize his union with Christine, a beautiful blonde, a clever woman, who said of him, with her German accent:

"The plack tevil gives me plack children and names them tevil's names."

Now she was an old woman, crippled with rheumatism, infirm, wrinkled; and he was a relic from Peter's days, a man of another age, whom people came to see as a curiosity. Before very long he must die, die and go up there, to stand before the God of the whites.

The old black barin knocked with his cane. The two footmen came running and lifted him up by the armpits. Very slowly they made their way up the steps to the wooden portico, and the door shut heavily behind them.

The Song

VASILI LVOVICH PUSHKIN WAS
in a bad humor. He had just traveled more than a thousand
versts in a wretched post berlin to come and put his scape-
grace of a nephew in the new "lyceum" (no one yet knew
whether the word was masculine or feminine in Russian)
established by His Majesty, Czar Alexander I.

His traveling companions had been the aforesaid nephew
Alexander (Sashka to his intimates), a serf girl whom he
had made his mistress, two valets, and his cook Vlas, whom
he insisted upon calling Blaise. He expected to spend three
or four months in St. Petersburg—time enough to absorb
the atmosphere of the capital and to get a short-skirted coat
made (everyone was wearing them now); then he could return to Moscow bursting with court news, with his hair
dressed in the latest fashion, with a new supply of epigrams,
cravats, perfumes, gossip—in short, with such a store as
would make him the star of the Moscow salons for at least
a month.

But the journey had tired him. He was no longer young.
His hair, which he wore in the style modeled after the
busts of the Emperor Titus, was growing thin. When he
spoke saliva spattered on his hearers through the gaps be-

tween his remaining teeth. He was getting fat, and the present fashion of tight trousers and cutaway coats emphasized his growing belly.

Then, too, he found coachmen and inn servants insolent. Since the French Revolution the rabble were raising their heads everywhere. Of course the scoundrels could not know that they were in the presence of a poet whose verses circulated orally and even in manuscript through every salon in Moscow. But he was a gentleman, and—damn it!— that ought to be enough! His family, which belonged to the old nobility, the real nobility, was no longer wealthy or much in favor at court. But the Pushkins had written their name on the most glorious pages of Russian history, and he himself had done that which would make him live in the memory of mankind. A poet, he had not hesitated to subject himself to the trials of a long journey in order that he might drink at the very fountain of inspiration: Paris. He had haunted the arcades of the Palais-Royal and had studied diction with Talma. He had even had the honor of being presented to the First Consul. They might call him "the Ogre" and "Buonaparte" now; nevertheless, it had been a flattering moment.

That journey to Paris, his life's master work, had given him a long tenure of favor among the hostesses of the fashionable salons. He permitted the ladies to smell his hair perfumed with Huile Antique. And the chaise longue he had had made after his return was exactly like the one on which Madame Récamier had posed for David.

But all that was long ago. . . . To make himself interesting again he had undertaken this journey to St. Petersburg. Yes . . . But Alexander here, Sashka, just what did he represent? Vasili Lvovich raised his eyeglass to his left eye, which was a little shortsighted, and looked hard at his nephew. The boy quickly dropped his blue eyes. Vasili Lvovich looked away. It was as he had thought: a purely African temperament. The boy's mother was the granddaughter of the Moor of Peter the Great.

Alexander had gone back to gazing at the depressing northern landscape: three quarters sky and one quarter flat ground. Until now he had always lived in Moscow, in one wooden house after another, at the end of a vast court where grass came up between the cobblestones. The family often moved, but it was always the same: on the ground floor a drawing room full of gilded armchairs and costly knick-knacks in glazed cases; upstairs, the room in which they lived—bare, cold, and never very clean. He had left home without regret. He felt like crying only when he thought of one person, his nurse. *Nyanya*, dear nyanya . . . Right now she must be lying dead drunk in the maids' room, where she was always locked up when she had drunk more than she should. She was the only one who loved him in all that great house, where people were always screaming and china was always crashing.

And there was Grandmother, Maria Alexeevna, a Pushkin, too, and thus her own son-in-law's cousin. She was the only member of the household who had any common sense. Her room was warm and clean, and there were pots of preserves in the cupboards: "Mirabelle Plums, 1807"; "Strawberries, 1808."

Alexander loved her domestic paradise. When he was little he used to make himself comfortable in the big basket in which she kept her woolens, and listened, gently lulled by her beloved voice: "Once upon a time there were a king and a queen . . ."

Or Grandmother would tell the story of her life and how she had married Osip Hannibal, the son of the Moor. He was handsome, even though he was black. He had married against the old Negro gentleman's will. After the wedding Osip wanted to present his young wife to his father. They had left their coach at the entrance to the manor and had crossed the court on foot as a mark of respect. Grandpapa Osip had impressed it on her that she must fall on her knees before the Moor, but she had not had time. She had fainted with fear when she crossed the threshold of the room in which her father-in-law was waiting. While Grandmother, stretched out in her pink taffeta panniers, was being brought to, the old Negro had overwhelmed his son with reproaches.

Well-deserved reproaches . . . Grandmother sighed, for the handsome half-breed had turned out to be a very poor husband and a wretched father. Their little daughter Nadezhda was not yet two when he abandoned them both for a drab, that Ustinya Tolstoi, who robbed him and ate up his revenue and ruined him with her clothes and jewels and silver-gilt dishes. While she, Grandmother, was almost dying of hunger he laid out French gardens for his mistress.

He ended by marrying the creature—using forged documents—while his legitimate wife was still alive. Well, bigamy was a tradition in the family. Old Hannibal himself had had two living wives.

But the Empress took a hand in the matter, sent Grandfather Osip to prison, and gave Nadezhda back to her mother, so that the Semiramis of the North was indirectly responsible for Alexander's birth.

Grandmother and her daughter lived together in St. Petersburg. With their miserable thirty-odd souls they could not pretend to be anything but poor. But Nadezhda had French governesses and learned to play the harpsichord. She developed into a lovely girl with black hair and fiery eyes. She was known in society as "the beautiful Creole" and "the beautiful African." She was impulsive, bad-tempered, fantastic, and domineering. Grandmother was quite in terror at having given birth to such a daughter of Africa. Her strange fits of inanition suggested something tropical. She spent whole days shut up in her room, biting her nails, her hair undone, her body barely covered by an India-print dressing gown. Then again she became the young lady of fashion who chattered French and played Grétry on the old harpsichord with its yellow teeth.

It was the period when pallor, high waists, and the waltz were coming into fashion. Nadezhda wore white dresses from Paris, kissed her intimates on both cheeks in the French manner, instead of bowing low from the waist according to the old Russian custom.

One day Sergei Lvovich Pushkin, an officer in the guards, fell in love with her and married her. He was a distant cousin of Grandmother's and so in a sense his own wife's uncle. Like his brother the poet, he liked above all things to shine in society, to act, and to recite poems. He was superstitious and a Voltairian, a member of the Shield of the North lodge and a churchgoer. His soul was as scanty as his knee breeches.

There was one unforgettable memory in his life. One day at a court ball the Emperor had come up to him and asked him why he was not dancing.

"I have lost my gloves, sire," Sergei Lvovich stammered.

"Here are mine," said the Czar. "Go and dance, young man."

Sergei Lvovich found everything difficult. He left the army to look after his estates and left his estates to do nothing. To live on his income gave him trouble enough. Once married, his first thought was to send in his resignation and retire on a pension in order to devote himself to the difficult task of occupying his leisure time. There was a tragedy in his life. His brother had beaten him in the race for fame. His married life had been a disappointment. He had imagined it as a perpetual voyage to Cythera, relieved by a succession of social engagements. But the voyages to Cythera had consequences with which he had not reckoned: Nadezhda was frequently pregnant. She was a wretched housekeeper. There were never enough sheets or blankets or silver. Yet Sergei Lvovich had a thousand souls in the province of Pskov. Only he would have had to pay some attention to them, go there, insist on the steward's rendering an accounting. He preferred making a scene at the dinner table when someone broke a glass worth fifty kopecks. When they had guests they borrowed forks from the neighbors. But Nadezhda wore fashionable dresses made of "pigeon's breast" muslin, with high waists.

Their first child was a daughter, Olga. Next came a boy, Alexander. On the day he was born Russia was celebrating. The bells of Moscow, the city of forty times forty churches, pealed for hours on end. The Emperor was joyful. He had become a grandfather. The Czarevitch's wife had just given birth to a little girl. The same day in Moscow another young mother was lying asleep on the ground floor of a huge house that looked like a shed (as a matter of fact, it had been a shed and had been made over into a house). Nadezhda's black curls, damp with the sweat of her labor, lay in disorder on the pillow.

Sergei Lvovich entered the room on tiptoe. He disliked hearing cries of agony and had left as soon as the labor pains had begun. Hearing her husband's steps, Nadezhda opened her eyes.

"Who is it?" she asked.

"It is I, my angel," he answered in French. "How do you feel?"

The newborn infant was wriggling and clenching his little brown hands in a wicker basket beside his mother's gilt bed. Sergei Lvovich bent and kissed him on the forehead, for he always remembered the proper thing to do. "We shall name him Alexander, after my grandfather," he said, turning to Nadezhda.

"The one who cut his wife's throat?" she asked, and made a face.

Sergei Lvovich frowned. He disliked being reminded of that episode in the history of his family. But Nadezhda had turned her face to the wall.

"Do as you like, my dear. I don't care."

She felt no tenderness for the child to whom she had just given birth. He reminded her too strongly of her yellow palms and her hair, which was that of a half Negress. At least Olga had a white skin. But she could not continue her reverie. Sergei Lvovich's mother was announced.

Nadezhda raised herself with an effort as a mark of respect. The old lady seldom came to her son's house. She reproached him for having married a girl without a dowry, and a "Creole" to boot. In her day gentlemen married white women, who brought them money, linen, and souls. But the younger generation had changed all that. Nowadays women's dresses revealed the shape of their hips; the French had cut off Louis XVI's head and had put in his place a general with an impossible name—she could never remember it—who was married to a sort of Negress himself.

She had lived through a long life and not always a happy one—and it was to see these godless days. Her husband, the late Lev Alexandrovich Pushkin, had been a hard man. His first wife had died in the private dungeon in which he had shut her up for being unfaithful to him. As for her lover, a French tutor who taught their children manners and the language of Racine, the outraged husband had hanged him without ceremony at the door of his manor house.

She herself had experienced a little of everything in her life with this nobleman of the old school. When she was about to give birth to her Sergei he had asked her to go with him to a reception at a neighbor's. She did not dare to refuse. Her maids dressed her in her panniers, a powdered wig, and her diamonds. She could hardly stand on her swollen legs; her feet were forced into satin shoes with silver buckles.

She felt the first pains in the coach. She was brought back home half dead and gave birth in a panniered dress, with diamonds around her neck and patches on her painted cheeks.

Now she was a widow and a grandmother. She kissed her daughter-in-law and looked at the infant through her chased lorgnette.

"I cannot congratulate you on his looks, my dear," she could not refrain from saying.

Nadezhda blushed slightly. "Take him away," she said to the servants.

Nadezhda Osipovna did not love her son. As for Sergei Lvovich, his children left him indifferent. He would entirely forget that he was a father except when, at some reception, it suited him to throw out a sentence full of exquisite sensibility, which he had lifted from *Emile*. As for Nadezhda, she did not even take the trouble to hide her lack of interest in her son. When they were together it seemed impossible that such a beautiful woman could have such an ugly child. Consequently they were seldom seen together.

She continued to bear children. After Alexander came two boys, Nicholas and Lev, who was called "Léon," because they spoke French even at home among themselves. Léon was white and cheerful and laughed a great deal. She loved him as suddenly as she had taken a dislike to Alexander.

Until he reached the age of eight Alexander was a fat, apathetic child. He often dropped things that were handed him. When he was given a handkerchief he immediately lost it. Nadezhda, who had not read *Emile*, pinched him as a punishment with the long, hard fingers that were her heritage as a quadroon. He had inherited from her the habit of biting his fingernails. To cure him she tied his hands behind his back and left him so for a whole day. When things were more than he could bear he took refuge with his nyanya or in the woolen basket in his grandmother's room (Maria Alexeevna was his grandmother on his mother's side).

At the age of two he became acquainted with the Romanovs. His nyanya used to take him walking in the Yusupov garden, a green paradise, the home of the white statue people. . . . One day there they encountered the Emperor Paul, who was said to be mad. In her fright the nurse forgot to take off Alexander's cap. The Emperor knocked it off his head with a sweep of his riding crop. Alexander's relations with the imperial family had had a bad beginning.

At eight he grew thin, became as limber as a whip, and noisy. He learned to know love, insanity, and death at an early age.

Grandmother had bought a small estate named Zakharovo, not far from Moscow. There they spent the summers: a wooden house, a big garden where preserves were made out in the open, and a wretched village of a few dozen souls, which did not even boast a church.

On Sundays they went to hear Mass in the next village, which had belonged to Boris Godunov and where the girls danced round dances on the evenings of market days. The children stayed on with only their nyanya, for Nadezhda and her freemason of a husband left immediately after the service, disdaining the amusements of the rabble.

Zakharovo sheltered a mad kinswoman of theirs, an unfortunate girl upon whom fear was being tried as a cure. One day a pail of water was thrown over her without warning. The insane girl ran down the stairs in her chemise, her long uncombed hair trailing after her like a black scarf. Alexander was musing in the garden.

"Brother, brother," she cried. "They think I am a fire—look, they've thrown water on me!"

Sergei Lvovich was fond of telling this story in the salons he frequented. According to him, Alexander, who was nine, had answered gallantly:

"No indeed, Cousin. They think you are a flower that needs to be watered."

Nicholas, Alexander's little brother, died the same summer. At first Alexander took no interest in his illness, then he felt sorry for his little brother and wanted to kiss him.

Nicholas stuck out his tongue. Not long after he died. He was buried in the little cemetery of the village where they went to hear Mass. Nadezhda walked behind the coffin, straight, gloomy, dry-eyed. Behind her came Sergei Lvovich, half fainting, leaning on two serfs who held his arms, his face swollen.

Autumn came. Alexander spent whole days in the garden. He was delighted with everything: the yellowing crowns of the trees, where the wind made a sound like silk, the sour smell of fallen leaves rotting under the rains. He was haunted by obscure melodies, by torturing rhythms that left him exhausted and happy, as if he had recovered from a fever.

That year they were to have a new tutor. The previous one, a French refugee, the Comte de Montfort, had been dismissed for seducing a serf girl. They had had an Englishwoman, Miss Belley, a German, and even a Russian, "Monsieur" Belikov. Everything was done to give them a perfect education—in other words, to teach them to speak French as if it were their mother tongue.

Alexander was not happy. His mother liked Léon better. His father paid no attention to him. Fortunately there were books. Without anyone's knowledge he devoured his father's library—that is, Corneille, Molière, Racine, Boileau, Voltaire, Rousseau, Diderot. He even read the first stammerings of Russian literature: Karamzin's *Poor Lise,* Derzhavin's odes, Zhukovski's ballads. Then he reached the secret shelves where Sergei Lvovich kept Chamfort, Grécourt, *La Pucelle*—mementoes of the time when he was a roué, with his hair dressed in "dog's ears," and mad about Parny, "'pon my word!"

His cheeks burning, his breath coming short, Alexander

read Delille, Scarron, Vergier, Grécourt. It was erotic poetry, illustrated with licentious engravings in which plump shepherdesses fell on the grass in a cloud of skirts when beribboned shepherds touched the treasures that swelled beneath their bodices.

> *Danis with humble words but bolder look*
> *Courted Zélire; now here, now there, he took*
> *A kiss as honey sweet, but would not rest*
> *Till he had touched the treasure of her breast. . . .*

His heart beat almost to bursting. . . . In his veins ran the hot blood of his African ancestors; he was a young god, an ardent, impetuous faun, like the ones in the forbidden engravings.

Forbidden? Why? . . . The mysteries of love . . . Obscurely he anticipated them, divined them with all his warm, muscular body. Women . . . Already their softness, their odor, the strange secret of their forms preoccupied and troubled him. Ah, to be big, to be strong. . . . When would he ever reach sixteen?

Meanwhile, he had two secrets. First, he was in love. His love obviously had no connection with that of the forbidden engravings. No, it was tender, pure, elevated. The object of it was Katya Sushkov, a lanky blond little girl with whom he danced at Iogel's. Every Thursday Monsieur Rousseleau, the new tutor, took them to Iogel's. Iogel was the best-known dancing master in Moscow. Olga was dressed *à la Grecque,* in a draped tunic cut from an old dress of Nadezhda's, and he and Léon wore full Turkish trousers.

Iogel was an old German who wore a powdered wig, knee breeches, and buckled shoes, like Monsieur de Voltaire in his portraits. He played a little pocket violin. Now and then he would stop and beat time with his foot and his bow:

"One, two, three; one, two, three; one turn in place!"

As for Katya, Alexander did not know much about her. She always came with an English governess. Once she introduced him. He brought his heels together and bowed, and the governess gave him a piece of gingerbread.

Second: he was writing poetry. Yes, now he knew how to quiet the fever of rhythm that obsessed him. All he had to do was to put words that rhymed at the end of every line: *amour—toujours;* or *amour—le jour; françois—reçoit.*

It goes without saying that he wrote in French, for he did not even know that one could write in any other language. It was in this fashion that he wrote a comedy, *The Pickpocket,* and even performed it for his sister. He was director, scene painter, actors, and prompter, and Olga was the audience. But the audience said that the play was rubbish, whereupon he composed the following quatrain:

> *The house at the* Pickpocket's *opening kicked*
>   *Up a terrible row. And it's clear*
> *That the author deserved it, his play being picked*
>   *From the pocket of one Molière!*

One day Sergei Lvovich said to his wife, "My angel, how old is Sashka?"

His angel thought for a moment and answered, "He must be eleven."

Sergei Lvovich rubbed his temples with the air of someone making a strong mental effort.

"Perhaps it is time to send him to boarding school."

"What for? Monsieur Rousseleau is giving him an adequate education. Besides, my dear, you are not unaware that the state of our fortune forbids us any unnecessary luxuries."

Sergei Lvovich never lost an opportunity to display his paternal sentiments. He remembered *Emile* and said feelingly:

"My angel, I shall never cease to sacrifice myself for my children. The days when to be well born was a sufficient recommendation for a career are over. The Emperor now surrounds himself with men of the Third Estate." (He wanted to say "with upstarts" but felt afraid and refrained. He was referring to Speranski, Alexander I's favorite.) "That sort of man tries to make up for his humble origin by a show of learning."

The sentence pleased him. He made a short pause.

"Nowadays, to get the smallest *chin,* you have to know mathematics and heaven knows what else." (Sergei Lvovich regarded mathematics with a feeling of aversion mingled with respect. He had never been able to progress beyond the Rule of Three.)

Nadezhda said nothing. He stopped in front of her.

"These are matters that women cannot understand, my angel."

It was decided that Alexander was to go to the Jesuits' school in St. Petersburg. The school was expensive, but the Jesuits were in fashion. The fine flower of the empire, the Gorchakovs, the Trubetskois, the Dolgorukis, had their Orthodox sons brought up by Catholic monks. But Alexander escaped the Jesuits.

"Why not the lyceum?" his uncle Vasili Lvovich had said in the course of the family council that followed Sergei Lvovich's conversation with his wife.

The lyceum was to open in the autumn. It was rumored

that the Emperor intended to have his own brothers, the Grand Dukes Nicholas and Michael, educated there. Corporal punishment was forbidden by the regulations. Something unheard of!

Vasili Lvovich took it upon himself to put his idea into execution.

"Trust him to me!" he had said to the Pushkins, and he had put his fat hand on Alexander's curly head.

Such was the childhood of the greatest of Russian poets. He had been taught French and manners, spelling, and even dancing. His education was complete. They had forgotten to teach him only one thing: his mother tongue.

ii

> *I'm a graceless young fellow*
> *Still going to school—*
> *No hypocrite I,*
> *And likewise no fool.*
>   My Portrait

On October 19, 1811, His Majesty the Emperor Alexander arrived at his summer palace, Tsarskoe Selo, early in the morning to open a lyceum intended for boys of good family.

His minister, Speranski, had himself devised the regulations of this privileged establishment, which was honored by the Czar's particular interest. The Czar had even proposed to have the grand dukes, his brothers, educated there, but the Empress Dowager had opposed a project that seemed to smell a little too strongly of the French Revolution.

The Emperor himself was recovering from his democratic illusions. It was even rumored that Speranski's position was no longer entirely secure. An ally and friend of Napoleon's since Tilsit, the Czar now dreamed of annihilating him. But a war with the victor of Austerlitz and Friedland required minute preparation. He thought of it day and night. No one suspected the change that had taken place in his ideas. The Czar was deceitful by nature and he had learned to dissimulate.

Consequently this "lyceum" no longer had the slightest interest for him. All these fine ideas about a liberalized education were in essence nothing but a means of subversion. He had recovered completely—even from Rousseau. Yet he had kept his promise: he had given up a wing of his palace to house the thirty pupils and he had come to open the establishment in person.

He turned all these things over in his mind during the ceremonies, sitting in the front row at a table covered with red cloth. His face, with its regular features (since the adultery from which his line had sprung, the dynasty produced only heavy and handsome men), wore an expression of polite boredom. He read the charter granted to the new lyceum in a monotonous voice. After that came the speeches, in which the pupils were referred to as the future pillars of the state. The Czar glanced indifferently at the boys, who stood in three rows to the right of the table. In their dress uniforms, with the white knee breeches (another of Speranski's ideas), they looked awkward. They were not the gilded youth of the empire, the fine flower of the Russian aristocracy, but the sons of provincial noblemen who had had influence enough to place their heirs in a school where they would be educated at the country's expense. The Czar stifled a yawn and turned away.

The speeches were over. He invited the empresses to visit the establishment. The old Empress Maria was fat and dark; the young Empress was blond and had prominent collarbones. (In his heart of hearts he thought her too thin. Was that why she had borne no children?)

When they reached the dining room they found the future pillars of the state at dinner. The Empress Dowager advanced toward one of the boys and asked him in her German accent: "Iss it a goot soup?" "Yes sir," stammered one of the boys in terror, unaware that he had mistaken her sex. She smiled and moved on.

The Czarevitch Constantine, heir to the throne, was busily pulling his sister's hair in a corner. He had by far the worst manners of any boy present.

At four o'clock the torches on the balcony of the new lyceum were lighted, forming the Emperor's initials. As the future pillars of the state played in the snow in the torchlight the Emperor called for the imperial carriages and left the lyceum. He never set foot in it again until the first class graduated.

The refectory buzzed like a hive with stifled conversation, laughter, and the clink of glasses. The monitors, who also acted as servants (they were usually old soldiers; the boys called them the "uncles"), waited at table and snuffed the candles. One of them passed between the tables with a kettle as big as a wash boiler and poured tea into their glasses.

Suddenly the door opened and the director, Malinovski, entered. He was a short, bald man, the author of a plan for an international tribunal intended to maintain peace by arbitrating conflicts between nations. His new duties frightened him. He cleared his throat and said:

"Gentlemen, I have an announcement to make. Hmm— an announcement that perhaps you will not care to hear. . . . His Majesty desires that the students shall not leave the lyceum throughout their entire course of study. Hmm. Not even during vacations."

He looked at the boys over his gold-rimmed spectacles and made a gesture indicative of his powerlessness. The boys stared into their plates. A few cried at the idea of not going home for the whole six years. Pushchin, a big, placid boy who sat next to Alexander, was one of them. The tears ran down his fat, wholesome face and dropped into his plate. Alexander looked at his new friend in astonishment. The announcement had aroused no feeling in him whatever.

He lived entirely in the present. The park delighted him most of all. The park of Tsarskoe Selo was very beautiful, a little neglected, spacious, full of birds and sounds and ponds and statues and little harmless snakes that slipped through your fingers when you tried to catch them. The palace, on the contrary—yellow and built in the style of Potsdam—was hideous. The wing in which the lyceum was situated was that in which the grand duchesses lived until they married.

Catherine had loved Tsarskoe Selo. She would come there to rest from the cares of government, to read Monsieur de Voltaire's letters, and to plant roses. There were so many roses that a certain part of the park had been named the Rose Field, and this became the favorite resort of the boys at the lyceum. There they walked and fought and played and, in winter, threw snowballs. Sometimes they even studied their lessons there.

A broad beam of light poured obliquely into the classroom through a gap in the clouds that revealed the blue lining of the sky. The light traveled slowly and with cold curiosity over the portrait of the Emperor and the icon of Our Lady of Kazan; it grazed several of the boys' heads and finally made a golden pool near the blackboard.

"Monsieur Pushkin, come to the blackboard."

Monsieur Pushkin stood up and went forward with studied deliberation.

"What does x equal?"

The future pillar of the state picked up the chalk and looked at the equation. He had a horror of mathematics.

"X equals zero," he said without conviction.

"Very strange indeed, Monsieur Pushkin. In my course everything ends in zero—for you. . . . Return to your place and go on with the poem you are writing."

The professor of mathematics was a man of the world. He did not carry his arithmetical fanaticism to the point of declaring war on the fine arts.

The founders of the lyceum had hoped to make its pupils into walking dictionaries. No subject seemed to be omitted from the curriculum. There were Russian, Latin, French, religion, moral philosophy, logic, arithmetic, algebra, trigonometry, physics, history, geography, chronology, rhetoric, the fine arts, law, ethics or sociology, political economy, archaeology, statistics, numismatics, aesthetics, hydraulics, and even the art of fortification.

No one learned more than a quarter of it all, and that badly. There was a dearth of professors. Those who had been found were students fresh from the University of Göttingen, adventurers come to Russia to make a fortune: a strange assemblage of writers, sharpers, philosophers, and freemasons. Hauenschild, an Austrian who had come to Russia to found a Masonic lodge for Orthodox priests, taught German in French because he did not know Russian!

The professor of French went under the name of De Boudry, but actually he was Marat's own brother. He was a hunchback and quite as ugly as the famous Friend of the People. His shirt collar was always greasy. He affected an air of Jacobinism, but the snuffbox he carried was a present from the "tyrant" and bore his portrait embellished with diamonds.

The boys were taught a little of everything, even dancing and fencing. After all, they were not merely future officials but also future men of the world. In winter they went skating on the lake or got up sleighing parties to points in the environs of the imperial residence. In summer the court changed Tsarskoe Selo into a miniature capital, humming with intrigues and social functions and the pursuit of pleasure.

The boys lived in close touch with the palace, from which the lyceum was separated by a glazed gallery. And every day about twilight they saw a corpulent figure cross the velvet lawns of the park, followed at a respectful distance by two policemen in disguise. It was the most virtuous mon-

arch in Europe going to visit his mistress, Mademoiselle
Veillot, a girl of sixteen.

Alexander undressed, snuffed his candle, reached under
his pillow, and pulled out a volume of French poems. Freed
of his long gilt-buttoned frock coat, which made him look
like a *chinovnik,* he appeared as he was: a slim, muscular
adolescent, not very tall, but strong. In one leap he could
mount to a table top to recite and he could jump over a
chair with only one hand on its back to steady him. He was
as agile as a monkey. And "Monkey" was the nickname he
had been given. He was also called "Frenchman" because
at times he even talked French in his sleep.

There was no sympathy in these nicknames. It was the
year 1813. "The Ogre," "the Corsican," "Buonaparte"—
in a word, Napoleon—had invaded Russia without declaring
war. Every day detachments of soldiers bound for the front
passed before the windows of the lyceum: melancholy and
innumerable silhouettes in their long winter cloaks (the
men who were being disciplined could be recognized by
the fact that they had no cloaks—a terrible punishment). It
was as if the blood of Russia flowed past their windows, the
thick blood of the muzhiks whom the provinces were pouring out. And still Napoleon advanced. Cylinder hats, after
the fashion of Paris, were forbidden. A strange thing:
French was no longer heard in drawing rooms. But how
oddly Russian sounded on the ladies' lips! Since Catherine's
time people of fashion had spoken nothing but French, except when addressing a servant.

Alexander sighed. He was not liked. He was too violent,
too incomprehensible. Fortunately there was poetry. The
new century had a deep love for the things of the mind, a

cult of beauty which made art of whatever it touched. The empire had brought the noble simplicity of straight lines and plane surfaces into fashion. In literature the trend was back to the classics.

At the lyceum everyone wrote verses. Illichevski composed fables; the lazy Delvig tried his hand at odes; and Küchelbecker, a martyr to literature, was compiling a dictionary into which he copied articles from the newspapers by hand: V—"On Virtue"; P—"On the Poems of Anacreon." It was a flowering of sonnets, a profusion of epigrams, a glut of madrigals. The style was noble, the sentiments lofty. A wind was called a "zephyr"; sleep, "Morpheus"; a nun was a "vestal," and love always a god. In this commonwealth of rhymes Alexander was king. In the verses that flowed with such marvelous facility from the fifteen-year-old schoolboy's frayed goose quill there was a lightness, an elegance, a purity, which made the Karamzins and the Derzhavins— the fathers of Russian literature—shake their heads. His poems appeared in the *Monitor* and in the *Sage of the Lyceum*, parodied magazines "Published by Danzas" (Danzas copied them out in his fair round hand). And not long since he had begun to send poems to the magazines, the real ones. "To a Fellow Poet," by A.N.k.sh.p. (a transparent pseudonym), had appeared in the *European Monitor*. . . .

He thought in verse. Sometimes verses came to him in his sleep. Inspiration swept down on him like a windstorm. He gnawed his goose quill, knit his brows. Everything around him vanished. He was like the pythoness, an empty shell, a temple inhabited by a mysterious god.

The father of Russian literature, the bard of Catherine II, Derzhavin, had become only a still-living relic. He was

Klopstock and Corneille, Milton and Parny, all in one. But the taste of the day was for melancholy, for English gardens and Ossian and the Middle Ages. Alexandrines and the sublime were no longer in fashion. Nevertheless, his authority was great.

On January 1, 1815, his two valets helped him into a pair of fur-lined boots (the blood chilled quickly in his old legs, stiff with gout), wrapped him in a fur cloak, and carefully seated him in a sleigh. The coachman jerked the reins. The horses began to trot through the snow that was yellowed by horse droppings.

The father of Russian literature drowsed. His errand reminded him of something. This road to Tsarskoe Selo—how many times had he not traveled over it to pay his court to the Semiramis of the North? . . . But Catherine had been dead for a long time. Dead, too, her son Paul, offspring of an imperial adultery. He alone remained.

He arrived at the lyceum after several hours' traveling, chilled through and in a bad humor, his feet frozen in spite of the furs. From time to time a drop detached itself from his red nose and fell onto his ruffle. The attendants freed him of his wrappings and he appeared, in knee breeches and powdered wig, like the very ghost of the past. His first words were for the porter:

"You, there, point me the way to the privy, please."

A pupil who had come running to kiss the hand that had written *The Cataract* turned away, disillusioned, without having paid his tribute of admiration.

The Russian Corneille listened, half asleep, to the examinations in geography, mathematics, history. . . . Mathematics? History? Youth was very learned these days. Finally it was literature's turn. He heard his poems discussed.

He roused himself. His eyes glittered under his heavy white brows.

Suddenly he heard a name: Pushkin. Pushkin? It seemed to remind him of something. He raised his eyes and saw a slim adolescent with curly hair, whose breeches outlined his well-turned legs. The boy was looking at him out of big blue eyes that made a strange contrast to the rest of his appearance, which was almost that of a Negro. He raised his right hand and began to recite chantingly and a little monotonously, in a voice that trembled with emotion:

". . . the wind that slumbers on the leaves barely breathes. Like a majestic swan the calm moon moves through silvery clouds. The lily, king of the fields, flowers in his proud beauty. Nymphs sport in the somnolent waters of the lake. . . ."

That music, that slow, majestic rhythm—it was that curly-haired, monkey-faced boy who had produced them! The wretch! Derzhavin wanted to stand up on his old legs. He wanted to shout to the audience, to the minister, to all the officials sitting there with their shining buttons, not grasping the revelation. . . . He wanted to shout, "There stands the new Derzhavin!"; to kiss the boy and hand the torch of poetry on to him and invoke Apollo and the Muses. . . .

Suddenly Pushkin covered his face with his hands. Tears streamed wildly through his clenched fingers. Pushing his way among officials in uniform and ladies in trains, he fled without looking back. He could not be found again anywhere all that day.

iii

> *. . . Love then, for time flies on.*
> *Of these our happy days make we the best.*
> *Is it in chill old age*
> *A man shall feel love's fire in his breast?*

The Emperor Alexander was ready to take his walk. As he had grown stout he had acquired a sort of assurance. He was the conqueror of Napoleon, the soul of the Holy Alliance, the savior of Europe. The fate of the civilized world lay in his hands and Metternich's. The accusation of parricide which had hung over him was washed away. To Russians he would always be the man who had taken Paris.

His court was the most pious in Europe. He was known as "the Angel" because of his religious tendencies. He was on good terms with the Beyond. When he dined in company with his old friend, Mrs. de Krüdener (she was known as "the Russian Maintenon"; this flattered him, for he liked being compared with Louis XIV), she always had a third place set for the "invisible guest."

The valet tightened the corset over his fat white belly and helped him into a frock coat of fine English cloth. The Emperor was proud of his sober elegance. Surrounded by his brilliant aides-de-camp, he always looked perfectly simple, perfectly correct. He stepped out onto the stairs. The usual companions of his walks were his little dog Charlot and a minister of state. It was during these morning walks that the Czar discussed political matters. That day he had sent for Engelhardt, the new director of the imperial lyceum. (The first director, Malinovski, had been dead for some time.)

"I am displeased with your pupils," he said, stopping in front of a new species of rose that bore the name of an English queen. "They have now reached the point of attacking my wife's ladies in waiting."

Engelhardt smiled politely.

"Does Your Majesty refer to Pushkin's recent adventure?"

"Precisely. Princess Volkonski has complained to the Empress. What is at the bottom of all this, exactly?"

"It is a perfectly trivial matter, sire. My pupils were passing through the gallery that connects the lyceum with the palace to attend the concert that is given every evening in the park. You know that there is a very dark corridor there on to which the apartments of the ladies in waiting give. Suddenly Pushkin heard a door open. He supposed that it was Natasha, Princess Volkonski's maid, a young girl he is in love with. He flew to embrace her. Unfortunately it was Princess Volkonski herself."

"Your Pushkin appears to be a wild fellow. I have not forgotten the episode of the punch drinking that night, about which Razumovski told me in his time. . . . So he not only entices his young friends into drinking alcohol, but he has relations with the feminine personnel of the palace too. Is it not a case that calls for punishment?"

Engelhardt's face grew serious.

"Sire, Your Majesty will pardon me for speaking to Your Majesty frankly. Pushkin has faults, which I am the first to recognize. Let us not forget that he is of African descent. But his exceptional gifts demand a certain consideration.

Our greatest writers, Zhukovski, Vyazemski, see in him the hope of Russian literature. The other day Your Majesty's historiographer, Monsieur Karamzin, came to Tsarskoe Selo on purpose to see our prodigy."

"Yet the verses he composed on my return from Paris are hardly brilliant. . . . Here, Charlot!"

The Czar caressed his spaniel. So this young poet everyone was talking about could find no inspiration in the deeds of his reign? With what could he be reproached? With not having been present at Waterloo, where the Allies were victorious over Napoleon without the Russians? But would Waterloo have been possible except for him; possible had he not spent ten years uniting Europe against the Ogre? He crumpled the rose he had picked and threw it away.

Engelhardt walked on in silence, fearing that he had displeased the Czar. In his puritanical heart he considered Pushkin a libertine. He himself was in sympathy with the tone of the eighteenth century, which was virtuous and sentimental. He was, furthermore, a freemason, a liberal, and a disciple of Rousseau. He treated his pupils like a father. His duty was to defend Pushkin, but he did not like him. And Pushkin returned the compliment.

Alexander had resumed his walk. The sand crunched under his polished boots. He decided to dissimulate.

"So your advice to me is?"

"Clemency, sire."

"You are right. After all"—he remembered Princess Volkonski's thin lips and wrinkled neck and smiled slowly—"perhaps our old maid was pleased by the young man's mistake."

Pushkin did not suspect the storm that had passed over his head. He studied little and badly. His years at the lyceum were drawing to a close. It was a quiet, humane existence in the midst of an iron century. Once outside the walls of the lyceum and all gentle illusions of virtue and equality vanished under the fierce breath of reality. Injustice and slavery stared you in the face. Men owned other men. They could sell them wholesale or retail, parting mother and child, husband and wife. You could kill a serf under the knout; it was not a crime, but merely a loss, for souls meant wealth. And this after Montesquieu, after Voltaire, after Rousseau. After Schiller, who believed that society had reached its final degree of perfection. This, after the French Revolution.

Everyone felt that the present state of things was impossible, outworn, criminal. It was a vertiginous thought to attack autocracy and serfdom, those twin breasts of the Empire of the Czars. But since the Bastille there was no structure that men could not hope to raze. And this one was worm-eaten.

Despite the activities of a police that was everywhere, liberalism—that crime against the state—could not be rooted out. Even the army was infected. The air seemed unbreathable to young officers returning from a country where the inscription "Liberty, Equality, Fraternity, or Death" was being hastily obliterated from the walls.

A regiment of guards was stationed at Tsarskoe Selo. The boys at the lyceum (they were called, in mongrel French, "les lycéistes") would jump the wall and make friends with the hussars. Pushkin was one of them. He liked the champagne and the jokes and the long fraternal meals, the smoke and the passionate conversations about God, love, Metternich's policies, and the Czar's latest mistress.

The hussars were something more than young braggarts,

hotheads, and high livers. They were young officers who had clanked their victorious sabers over the cobbled streets of Paris and who had returned with their heads in a whirl from having breathed the air of liberty. There was Chaadaev, the soldier-philosopher, atheist and freemason, beautiful and cold as a fallen angel, who could have taken life on the good side but who preferred philosophical speculation. There was Kaverin, the child of fortune, who drank and sang and wenched and was handsome and gay and rich and noble. There was Raevski, who was sixteen, like Pushkin, and whose father, General Raevski, had led him by the hand into the battle against Napoleon in 1812.

Life at Tsarskoe Selo, in close touch with the court, did not inspire respect for the monarchy. The Czar was nothing but a crowned and anointed hypocrite who surrounded himself with old women, priests, and reactionaries. For him, praying to God and fooling mankind went hand in hand. He had fooled everyone: Napoleon, his own wife, his allies, his subjects.

At midnight, over the cigars and champagne, tongues were loosed, despite the severe eyes that watched them from the full-length portrait of "the Angel" in the uniform of a general. Nevertheless, the police were everywhere, even among the hussars.

Alexander read aloud *The Monk,* and *Barkov's Ghost,* callow poems into which he had put all the impure dreams that come to an adolescent boy who feels the first urges of puberty. Besides, licentious poems were in fashion. Everyone was imitating Vergier, Grécourt, and Scarron. But he no longer had to wear out his fevers in erotic poetry. He had learned to know love, the delicious and pacifying love of the body. His new virility no longer tortured him as he lay on his narrow dormitory bed through the nights of May, no longer made blue circles under his eyes. He had pressed a woman's thighs between his strong boy's knees, still marked with black-and-blue spots and the scars of scratches. His mistress was a young serf girl who had been made an actress, Natasha.

He went to the sham theater of Count Tolstoi, a great nobleman whose vast fortune permitted him to satisfy any passion. Count Tolstoi's passion cost him a great deal of money; it was the theater. His theater differed from a real one only in size. As soon as he appeared in his stage box, libretto in hand, the three raps sounded, and the heavy red-and-gold curtain—spun, woven, and embroidered by the peasant women on his estates—was pulled up.

The plays were *The Barber of Seville, The Village Sorcerer,* pastorals, and the kind of comic opera that takes place in an imaginary China. The count directed the rehearsals himself. There would be two or three performances, after which the count would be bored with the play and a new one would be put into rehearsal. The actors were serfs. When their acting was bad the count would have them cudgeled afterward. Natasha, a beautiful blond girl, was the star of the company and the count's mistress. She did not know what to do with her arms and came on the stage casting terrified glances at the stage box where her master sat, while a lackey disguised as a shepherd recited, all in one breath:

> *"But stay! I see Lisette*
> *Approach with timid feet.*
> *In flowers and flowerlike face,*
> *What charming colors meet!"*

Lisette's charms were as great as her acting was deplorable, and the full Turkish trousers of *Bajazet* were just as becoming to her as the panniers and the powdered wig of *The Marriage of Figaro*. She was applauded to the echo and had a crowd of visitors in the greenroom.

Alexander persuaded her to meet him in the park. Catherine's fantasy had sown it with dozens of little shelters, which were now forsaken and overgrown with greenery.

The ardent boy pleased Natasha. She was timid, he commanding. She allowed him a kiss; he bared one of her breasts. After all, she was only a serf turned actress and he was a barin, a gentleman, a Pushkin. He was impatient, gluttonous, charming. She murmured, "Monsieur Pushkin, you mustn't. . . . Monsieur Pushkin, that's wicked." But Monsieur Pushkin did not listen to her. He pressed her to him—this warm, soft, unknown thing, a woman. At last he was to learn the mysteries of love about which the books were forever talking. . . .

Their romance was short-lived. Costumes and scenery finally ate up Count Tolstoï's fortune, and the woman in whose arms the greatest of Russian poets first knew love was sold at auction like a filly.

He got over it. He had no time for regrets. He sucked in life through every pore in his skin. The *Russian Museum* and the *Son of the Fatherland* were publishing his verses. The court commissioned him to write an ode in honor of the Prince of Orange, a guest of the Emperor. He wrote it, and the Empress Dowager sent him a gold watch. In a sudden fury he ground it under his heel: he was the poet of liberty, and royal presents were not for him.

Karamzin, the great Karamzin, had come to Tsarskoe to see little Pushkin. (The great Pushkin was his uncle, Vasili

Lvóvich, but it began to be said that Alexander would out-
shine him.) Karamzin was stately and dressed entirely in
black. He wore a ruffle, knee breeches, and shoes with
buckles. He was a scholar and a courtier. His wife, in contrast—Catherine Andreevna—was charming. Alexander
wrote her a letter to tell her he loved her, but she burst out
laughing and showed it to her husband. Exasperated, he
turned away from her.

Maria Smith, whom he had met at Engelhardt's, at least
did not treat him like a boy. She was gay and witty and
elegant—a true Frenchwoman, nee Charon-Larose. She
granted him certain favors, and he at once proclaimed the
fact in his *Stanzas to Lydia*. But Lydia complained to Engelhardt. It came out that she was a widow and pregnant.
. . . Women were all alike. Not one of them could equal
his dear Bakunina.

On November 29, 1815, he wrote in his journal:

*I was happy—no, I was not happy, yesterday. In the morn-
ing, standing under her window, I was tormented by expectation. I looked down the snow-covered road with
inexpressible emotion. . . . I did not see her. At last, when
I had already lost hope, I encountered her unexpectedly on
the stairs. Sweet moment. . . .*

> *He sang of love, but ah! his voice was sad.*
> *Alas, he knew of love nought but its pains. . . .*
> ZHUKOVSKI

*How beautiful she looked, how well her black dress be-
came my adorable Bakunina! I have not seen her for eighteen hours. What a situation, what torment! But for five
minutes I was happy.*

He, too, knows nothing of love but its pains. He loves her so much that he faints at a touch of her hand. He waits and waits, standing in the snow, to see a delicate silhouette pass like a Chinese shadow-show puppet across a window.

Sometimes she came to the lyceum to see young Bakunin, her brother. All the boys were in love with her adorable little feet in the heelless slippers and with her black eyes that glistened moistly. She wore high-waisted voile dresses and velvet spencers that outlined her young bosom. She was the most charming of the Empress Elisabeth's maids of honor. Her dance programs looked like class lists; the name of every pupil in the lyceum was there. Iakolev was the most amusing, Korsakov the best musician, Pushkin the most in love. When he took her by the hand or the waist for a waltz or a mazurka he capered like a young stallion and so visibly lost his head that there were smiles all over the ballroom.

But the charming Catherine Bakunina cared nothing for her young adorer. She was twenty. All her friends had married. What her soft eyes sought so insistently through the ballrooms was a "marrying man." For her curly-headed page she had nothing but amused smiles. Sometimes she pressed his hand to thank him for pushing her sleigh or for fastening her skate on her little foot.

Alas, Catherine was gone now, and he sought in vain for traces of his beloved in the vast autumnal park. He wandered down the paths, where the wind swept along the dead leaves; he pressed his cheek against the great yellowing oaks and gave himself up to tears.

Catherine had gone without a kiss, without a look. But patience! In a few more months a new life would begin.

Another winter and he would be a grown man.

The Sonnet

YOUNG MR. PUSHKIN JUMPED
out of bed, put on the dressing gown his valet, Nikita, held
for him, and sat down at his toilet table to polish his nails,
of which he was proud. Yesterday, too, he had come home
long past midnight, after drinking more than he should,
losing at cards, and making half a dozen political puns,
the mildest of which could bring him into disgrace, perhaps
even send him to prison. Nevertheless, he felt fresh and
ready to begin all over again.

He looked at himself carefully in the mirror and, as always, felt dissatisfied with his face. His own description of
himself was a "descendant of deformed blacks." Nevertheless, women found something agreeable in his blue eyes,
his dark curls, his thick lips, his broad shoulders, and his
slim waist. He laughed with loud, contagious laughter,
throwing back his head and half choking. There was a
saying that Pushkin's laugh was a force of nature, that
when he laughed one could see his entrails. He had kept
his old habit of jumping onto tables.

Nikita looked at him in the mirror and smiled. Pushkin

remembered the halting French verses he had written at the lyceum, *My Portrait:*

> *My height, alas, is far below*
> *The height of taller men.*
> *My skin is fair, my hair is blond*
> *And curls and curls again.*

"And curls and curls again," he repeated, smiling. His hair was just beginning to grow back on his shaven skull under the wig dressed in the style known as "wind-blown." Love in the demimonde cost more than coin of the realm. In the course of two years he had caught the pox three times. This distinction won him the respect of "lions" and "dandies," or, to use the language of the past century, of the "gilded youth" who were to be found every evening at Madame Sophie's, drinking bad champagne (sold at exorbitant prices) and amusing themselves with her "boarders."

His official mistress was Olga Masson, a blond girl of the people, who drank vinegar to make her cheeks pale and wore blue dresses that matched the color of her eyes. It was an inconsequential and gay affair. Olga loved him and was unfaithful to him, as she was unfaithful to everyone, without a thought of harm. She could not understand his jealous rages. In addition there were a Nadezhda, a Miss Steingel, and a Polish girl named Angelica—other vague blond-and-blue shades.

He boasted of pleasing young beauties by the shameless violence of his desires. In his veins flowed the thick blood of Ethiopian princes and the no less excitable blood of Russian noblemen. It was an astonishing mixture. He had a furious need to expend himself. His friends, the poets of the new Romantic school, who were serious by nature and disillusioned by conviction, could not understand him and accused him of drowning his young genius in wine, of prostituting it with women, and of wasting it on trifling love songs. They reproached him with going out in society. Batiushkov, the Russian Lamartine, suggested sending him to Göttingen and feeding him for three years on bread and milk and logic.

At the recollection Alexander burst into that irresistible laugh of his which showed his Negroid teeth. Nikita handed him a cravat, and he tied it with studied negligence and moistened his handkerchief with perfume. The ritual of dressing was over. He went into the drawing room.

The Pushkins' apartment in St. Petersburg was as disorderly and dirty as their house in Moscow had been. The neighbors still furnished the spoons when there were guests, and Sergei Lvovich still liked to lean against the mantelpiece and recite Molière. He had grown even more miserly. For three months Alexander had been begging him to buy him a pair of the low dancing slippers that were in fashion. But Sergei Lvovich insisted on lending him his own, which dated from the days of Paul I.

As for the beautiful young girl in whom Alexander was surprised to recognize his sister's forgotten features, she wept in secret because she was obliged to wear old dresses that were too high in the waist and failed completely to set off her young bosom. Yet she was old enough to marry. . . .

As he passed through the room he stopped and glanced at the invitations: a ball at the Olenins', another at Princess Golitsyn's . . . He was in great demand. When his family was mentioned people said, "They are young Pushkin's relatives." As for himself, people forgave him everything:

his careless manners, his insolence, and even his terrible epigrams.

Two years earlier he had left the lyceum with a diploma which proclaimed that Pushkin, Alexander, had attended the imperial lyceum of Tsarskoe Selo for six years, that his standing in religion, Bible history, logic, philosophy, ethics, and civil and common law was good, in fencing, French, and Russian very good, and in conduct poor. His Gracious Majesty had at once deigned to take him into his service with the rank of "secretary" in the Ministry of Foreign Affairs at a salary of seven hundred rubles a year. He was seventeen. The Ministry of Foreign Affairs left him with plenty of leisure. As for his salary, it was just enough to pay for his seat at the theater and the brandied cherries that Olga loved.

He joined his family in the dining room and respectfully kissed his mother's hand. She had succeeded in breaking him of the habit of biting his nails, but her own were still gnawed to the quick. She was the same nervous and apathetic woman, except that no one now called her "the beautiful Creole." Her elder son's success as a poet had not made him any dearer to her. Her favorite was still Léon. She looked at Alexander indifferently and rang for the servant, who presently brought him a poorly cooked and warmed-over meal.

Afterward he took his heavy silver-headed cane and went out. He liked walking and he had no money: two reasons for not taking a carriage. For the second time in his life he was living in St. Petersburg, a very different place from Moscow, with its wooden houses, its crazy pavements, its blind alleys, and its generally provincial look. Moscow had grown haphazardly, spreading in all directions at once. Here the will of man was felt everywhere: the streets crossed each other at right angles and the Neva flowed in a granite channel.

He entered the Nevski Prospect, which was to St. Petersburg what the boulevards are to Paris, what the Prater is to Vienna, and Pall Mall to London. It began to snow. He liked to stop at the shops behind some window-shopping woman who raised her skirt to reveal a narrow foot in heelless slippers tied with black ribbons crisscrossed over a white stocking. Lamps were already being lighted in the windows, as it grew dark here by two o'clock in the winter. Compared with this boreal capital, where the nearness of the North made itself felt, Moscow seemed almost the South.

Private carriages passed at full speed, the sound of the galloping horses muffled by the snow. One stopped, and a gloved hand lowered the window.

"Pushkin!"

Alexander turned. His friend Kaverin motioned to him to get in.

"To Talon's."

The coachman tightened the reins and the horses started. Talon was a French restaurateur whose establishment could be relied upon at any hour to provide truffles, Strasbourg pâté, and champagne, and whose French cuisine was served to an accompaniment of gypsy songs. You went there with a woman to sup in a private room, or with men for long fraternal feasts, after which you repaired to the theater. The bills were terrific, but Alexander never paid. His friends were rich and knew that he had no money. Sometimes it hurt his pride.

They arrived at Talon's. A footman took Kaverin's long

officer's cloak and Pushkin's Spanish cape. They sat down.

"I don't need to ask if you will be at Princess Golitsyn's tonight," Kaverin said, rubbing his hands which were numb with cold.

Alexander blushed slightly. His passion for this woman of forty, in whom the mystical flame of a great love seemed always to burn, was well known. She was a Russian Madame de Staël—with the advantage over her original of being a beauty. The wits and thinkers of her day met every night at her house. Her nickname was "Princess Nocturne" because she never rose until the lamps were lighted. Pushkin had dedicated eight celebrated verses to her, which devotion ruled out neither Nadezhda, nor Olga, nor any of the others.

He made a gesture of denial. "No, my dear fellow, Golitsyn is a thing of the past. And the proof is that tonight I'm going to the theater."

"Amen," said Kaverin solemnly, cutting his roast beef (the latest thing in food was rare meats and strong-smelling cheeses). "Your loves are short-lived. By the way, how is the ever-charming Angelica?"

"Vsevolozhski won her from me at cards, along with a volume of verses that I have not yet written. I hear that she was delighted. Anyway, I am tired of blondes. . . . Good day, Barkov!"

A group of young men who had just entered the celebrated restaurant were making their way to the table at which Alexander and his friend were sitting. Idle noblemen like themselves, they, too, belonged to the world in which one had liberal views and aristocratic prejudices, in which nothing was more highly esteemed than a well-turned sonnet or a well-directed sword thrust.

The last years of Alexander's reign had disappointed everyone: the rising generation, the army, the liberals. The Czar's favorite, Arakcheev, was transforming Russia into an immense guardhouse. Secret societies flourished everywhere. Some of them were frankly political, like the Union of Virtue. Others, like the Green Lamp, conspired under the pretense of literary activities. Their members met at night, after the theater, around a table covered with bottles, but when they broke up at dawn they had discussed the latest European developments and had criticized the government. Debauchery was part of the window dressing.

Waiters brought chairs for the newcomers.

"Are you coming to see Semenova tonight?" Alexander asked one of them.

"My dear fellow, I can't bear classical plays, and Semenova is no good in anything but *Athalie*."

"You mustn't say anything against Semenova in front of Pushkin," said Trubetskoi seriously. "She is his new passion. He would fight a duel for her. Speak up, Sasha, and admit that you are in love with her."

"She's beautiful enough for me to be in love with her," said Pushkin. "She has a great talent and small feet. I adore women with small feet. That's why I let Vsevolozhski have Angelica. She had feet like Queen Bertha's."

"I'd like to see a man who was not in love with Semenova."

"'*Tout Paris pour Climène a les yeux de Rodrigue*,'" declaimed one of the newcomers. "And all in vain! Gentlemen, Pushkin is boasting. Semenova is as virtuous as the statue of Modesty. Things have already reached the point where ladies are not what they were in the last century.

What in God's name is to become of us if actresses begin to imitate them?"

"A sad age!" sighed Kaverin. "Have you observed that even fashions are becoming dull? Black, midnight blue, bottle green—nothing but dark colors to be seen. The Emperor is bald and always wears black."

"He is in mourning for his illusions. . . ." Alexander laughed.

"Shhh, Pushkin, always indiscreet! You know the walls have ears."

"Why, no, my dear fellow, the times are no longer dangerous. The Neva has thawed and the Peter and Paul Fortress is cut off from the rest of the world, so one may say what one pleases. I am seizing the opportunity—the more so because communications with the prison are soon to be re-established!"

His companions burst out laughing. Pushkin was as indiscreet as a schoolboy. At a time when a man might be sent to Siberia for a word, he went to the theater and openly displayed a portrait of Louvel with the inscription, "A lesson for kings."

"You're coming to Olenin's this evening, Pushkin?" Chaadaev asked, lighting a cigar.

"No. Since severity, pallor, and political economy have become fashionable I avoid balls. No one talks about anything but Adam Smith and free trade. After all, Kaverin is right—a sad age. Is it not, Kaverin?"

"In my opinion. The world is growing old. Look at literature—it's a desert. Pushkin, give me your authoritative opinion. Do you like Monsieur de Châteaubriand?"

"I don't read prose," answered Pushkin, who was beginning to get drunk. "What an idea—writing prose!"

"And the Germans?" interrupted Chaadaev, who had attended the University of Göttingen. "After all, Goethe is a great poet. . . ."

"And Schiller is his prophet," said Pushkin, resting his feet on the back of a chair, so that his body formed a right angle. "The Germans will never have a great literature. Even their language is inharmonious. *Der, die, das*—I could never get it into my head. At our lyceum even German was taught in French. . . ."

"And here at home," Kaverin went on, pursuing his idea, "in the realm of literature we have Monsieur Katenin's articles——"

"I have nothing to say against Katenin," Pushkin interrupted; "he makes good puns."

"But society? For example, fifty years ago what did you find on a pretty woman's dressing table? Rousseau and *Les Liaisons dangereuses*. What do you find there today? Jung-Stilling, Ekkarthausen, Swedenborg, theosophists, mystics, and I don't know what all. The end of the world—there's our chief subject of conversation. Where do you find a lady at seven o'clock in the morning? In bed after a night of love? No—at church, listening to a Protestant pastor's sermon. And the clairvoyants, the fortunetellers——"

"Oh, fortunetellers—that's another matter," said Pushkin quickly. His face darkened.

Kaverin burst out laughing. "Pushkin defending fortunetellers, gentlemen! A highly interesting occasion!"

"A fortuneteller told me three things, two of which have already happened. I have every reason to believe that I shall not escape the third," said Pushkin sadly.

"What a tragic face. . . . And you really believe in

those old wives' tales? There's one of our freethinkers for you!"

"Judge for yourself. The other day I went to Mrs. Kirchhof's with some friends. She said to me: 'You will soon receive some money and have a business conversation. You will die young at the hands of a white-haired man.' *Weisskopf*—Chaadaev, you know German; that means 'white head,' doesn't it?"

"Yes," Chaadaev answered. "And after that?"

"On my way out I ran into Orlov. You know Orlov? He took me by the arm, reproached me for my dissipated life, advised me to enter the army, and finally proposed that I should accompany him back to his regiment. But that's nothing. When I got home I found an envelope containing money. A friend who had come into an inheritance had remembered a gambling debt that I had completely forgotten. . . . What do you think of that?"

Pushkin's story had produced a slight chill. Iakubovich, one of the newcomers, who was fair, tried to relieve it with a joke.

"Now I understand why Pushkin avoids me," he said, pointing to his hair. But the unpleasant impression remained. Iakubovich was the most celebrated swordsman in St. Petersburg. He would challenge a man to a duel for a yes or a no, and his reputation kept the youth of the two capitals from sleeping at night.

"It is late, gentlemen; we shall miss Semenova," said Kaverin. They left the restaurant. Cabmen, muffled in their wadded coats, were waiting outside for customers.

"To the Grand Theater."

Young men of good breeding were expected to appear at the theater several times a week in one of the first rows in the orchestra, to focus a disillusioned opera glass on the boxes, and to disappear with a yawn before the end of the fourth act. Even at their pleasures they wore an air of boredom.

Alexander's simian vivacity was ill suited to these exigencies. His witticisms, his impertinences, his boyish tricks traveled from mouth to mouth until they reached the ears of the police, who carefully collected Mr. Pushkin's jokes and epigrams and puns. Once he applauded by pounding on a neighbor's bald spot. His slim figure, his curly hair, his fifth finger with the long nail protected by a golden thimble were known to all the theatergoers of St. Petersburg.

They made a noisy entrance. Semenova had just come on the stage, swathed in a black tunic, and was declaiming:

"Whence comes this joy, to me with cares oppressed?
Whence this repose that softly fills my breast?"

Pushkin saw signals from a box in which there were two ladies. He hurried to the box, treading on people's feet.

"Come and sit with me, but only on condition that you will be good," murmured the younger of the two ladies, giving him her gloved hand to kiss.

"As good as a statue," Pushkin assured her, bowing. It was the young actress Kolosova, who had just made her debut in *Antigone* and who, it was said, would one day be as great in comedy as Semenova was in tragedy. She had come to measure her rival's popularity.

Alexander sat down by the beautiful actress and pressed her hand imperceptibly. She smiled and shook her finger at him.

"Pushkin, if you don't stay still I shall execute my threat."

"Which threat, goddess?"

"To cut your nails."

"You wouldn't do anything as wicked as that?"

"Of course I would."

"And I thought you were sensitive!"

"Why so?"

"Because I saw you crying in church at Easter. I was even much distressed to see you so unhappy. After all, there was no reason whatever for crying, since the Saviour had risen!"

"Pushkin! Is nothing sacred to you?"

"Of course, goddess. Beauty is sacred."

"Be still and let me listen."

Pushkin raised his opera glass, looked at the stage, and yawned. Semenova had gone off. A familiar little devil stirred in Alexander's heart. He wanted to do something comical, unexpected, insolent. Then, seeing the serious countenance of a well-known man, he took off his wig as if it were a hat, and bowed.

ii

Count Miloradovich sent a footman for one of those checked shawls that were imported from Scotland and called "plaids," wrapped himself in it, and lay down on the couch in his office. He had something to think about.

The governor general of St. Petersburg was vexed. A young official from the Ministry of Foreign Affairs, whom he had summoned for an interview, had just left his office.

Very annoying, this Pushkin matter. The young man came of a good family—old nobility, although not rich. One of the most talked-about young men in St. Petersburg. How often he had seen him in the greenrooms which he himself assiduously frequented!

Count Miloradovich was a "gentleman" himself (the English word had lately come into fashion), a devotee of the theater, a man of the world (though it is true that he had the reputation of speaking French badly—an unforgivable sin). He disliked denouncing men who moved in the same circles as himself. Why the devil did all the young men of good family have to be liberals?

However, he had heard that the Emperor was unfavorably disposed toward this erstwhile student at his lyceum. Had he not said to Engelhardt: "Pushkin is flooding Russia with subversive poems which the younger generation learns by heart"? And he was said to have threatened him with Siberia. The face of the governor general of St. Petersburg darkened. Perhaps he had acted too precipitately when he had told the young man that the government had pardoned him? He rang and ordered black coffee: it helped him to think.

The fact was that the fellow deserved punishment. His puns circulated clandestinely through the provinces and the two capitals. The highest personages in the state, the Czar himself (hard as it was to say it), were not safe from his acid intelligence. One day when a bear that had escaped from its cage was found loose in the park, where he might have fallen on the Emperor, Pushkin had said at the top of his voice in a crowded theater, "At last a man has been found, and it turns out to be only a bear!"

The count recollected their conversation. He had not

been displeased to have an opportunity of confronting this rare bird, this Pushkin, this great poet sprung from the soil of Russia. So that was he—that curly-haired youngster with the look of a page. The governor had expected to see a man bowed by disgrace. He saw an awkward youth who burst out laughing and showed two rows of big, healthy teeth. The count had spoken to him severely:

"Sir, by delivering to me of your own volition the subversive poems of which you are the author, you will spare your parents the disgrace of a search, which would not be to their taste, I am certain."

"Your Excellency's police will find nothing in my house. All my papers have been burned. But it is all written here." He pointed to his forehead. "If you will be good enough to give me paper I will write out everything I have composed up to now, except what has been published."

The count, who liked a gesture, could not refrain from exclaiming (he rather regretted it now):

"Ah, that is truly chivalrous!"

Pushkin had written for an hour. The result was there, in the notebook the count was still leafing through. His agents had gone to a great deal of trouble to bring him much less that he had just obtained so easily.

Pushkin had behaved like a gentleman, and Miloradovich wanted to return his politeness. He had told him that the faults of his youth would be blotted out. But what would the Emperor say? He was devious and spiteful. For the third time the count rang.

"My uniform," he said, "and my sword. Have the horses harnessed. I am going to the palace."

Alexander received him standing and heard him out impassively. How guess what was going on behind that cold white mask which was becoming heavy with age? Miloradovich cited Pushkin's popularity, alluded to the advantage that would accrue from a display of generosity toward the famous young poet, and exhibited the notebook. The Czar removed a finely shaped and well-kept hand from beneath his coattails and leafed through it.

For the second time he had wished to punish Pushkin. For the second time men who ranked among the most influential in the empire had intervened in his behalf. When he had heard of Pushkin's disgrace the historiographer, Karamzin, the Crown Prince's tutor, had donned his decorations and gone to the Empress to beg that Pushkin be pardoned. Now Miloradovich himself had come to intervene in his favor.

The Czar decided to temporize. Since he could not send Pushkin to the Solovetski Monastery he would banish him, at least, from St. Petersburg. The Czar raised his bald head and held Miloradovich with his heavy blue eyes.

"Since you have informed him of my forgiveness, there is nothing for me to do but to grant it. General Inzov, inspector general of colonists in South Russia, has asked me for young officials. Let us send Pushkin South. Travel educates young men."

The Poem

MARIA RAEVSKI LEANED
back in the carriage, closed her eyes, and sighed.
She was tired of looking out the window. For several
days now it had been the same landscape of steppes in
springtime.

To go to the mineral springs in the Caucasus was a real
journey. Progress was slow; behind you trailed a whole
general staff of nurses, governesses, valets, crowded into
coaches, on trunks full of clothes and packing cases full of
kitchenware, holding baskets of provisions on their knees.

The big black berlin, covered with leather, in which
Maria sat with her sister Sophia, their old nurse, and two
foreign governesses, was preceded by the lighter carriages
in which General Raevski and Captain Nicholas Raevski,
Maria's father and brother, were traveling. Sometimes,
tired of sitting, they mounted their horses and rode beside
the berlin. Maria, looking out the window, saw their tall,
broad figures and thought with pride of her heroic father,
who could have been a prince but preferred to remain a
soldier and who, when the Czar had wished to make him a
count, had answered with the Rohans' proud motto: "King
I cannot be, duke I disdain to be, I am a Rohan."

Napoleon had said of him that he was the stuff of which marshals were made. In Russia he was honored as a national hero, and his portrait, together with the Czar's and the usual India prints, was in every traveling merchant's pack. In 1812, with ten thousand men, he had held back Marshal Mortier's forty thousand veterans. It was said that when his soldiers flinched he had taken his two sons by the hands and cried: "Forward, my children! My sons and I will open a way for you!" But now he denied having made any such theatrical gesture, and whenever it was mentioned he always added in French, "And that is how history is written!"

Maria's adoring eyes moved from the general's tanned face to the open, careless face of her brother, the same whom he had led into battle—or so legend said—at the age of eleven, and who was now a captain in the hussars.

A year earlier she herself had been an adolescent—her figure too thin, her hair too heavy, her eyes too black, and her collarbones too prominent. But now the charming miracle had taken place. A woman had been born in the uneasy little girl. When she was asked her age she answered: "Fifteen." But everyone knew she was cheating and that she was really only fourteen. Southerners become women early, and Maria, through her mother, had Greek blood in her veins.

She knew she was beautiful in her own way, which was alive, passionate, unusual: thick curly hair, which she sometimes let fall over her shoulders like a black rain, short-sighted eyes that were veiled and caressing, an intelligent profile, and the willful, sensuous mouth of the Raevskis. In short, grace rather than beauty, temperament rather than perfection, seductiveness rather than regular features. . . . She was named Maria, like the Virgin and like every

chambermaid. Her friends had given her an exotic nickname, "the Daughter of the Ganges." But she was not
coquettish and she charmed everyone: her father, her
brother, this chance traveling companion, Pushkin—she
could often feel his eyes on her, on her black hair, on her
girlish breasts.

He managed to be in attendance whenever she got out
of the carriage, to give her his hand, to glimpse the end of a
little foot shod in a black slipper. She liked to listen to him
recite, but she was more diverted than moved. You could
not take a man like Pushkin seriously. He flirted with everyone, even with Sophia, who was only twelve.

Maria received his silent homage as her due: she was
beautiful; he was young and a poet. What could be more
natural than that he should adore her a little? But in his
heart, she felt sure, he loved only his muse. . . .

She pressed her forehead against the pane. Still the same
pale green steppe, but now on the horizon she could see a
glaucous patch over which swept the shadows of clouds.
Maria's heart raced: she had never seen the sea. The
road followed the coast, and now they could hear the
sound of waves falling on the beach and the fresh gurgle
of the water as it dragged the shingle back.

"Let's go and look at the sea!" Maria cried, and without
waiting for the two governesses to consent she called to the
coachman to stop.

The women got out. The sea wind, laden with sea odors,
seized Maria, pulled her dress tight against her young body,
and flapped her skirt like a flag. It was a warm, strong wind
that brought a taste of salt. She untied the ribbons of her
flounce-lined bonnet and ran into the wind toward the sea,
which was licking the blond beach. . . . She was a bac-

chante, a dryad drunk with wind and speed and sea scents. Her little feet leaped from stone to stone, until she stopped at last, out of breath. The sea, with its hem of foam, seemed to wish to lie down at her feet. Big smooth waves curled over a few feet from the beach, then broke with a thunderous sound and drew back, leaving a space of wet stone and sand. Maria heard the voice of the English governess calling her to come back, and she walked slowly up the beach, her exaltation collapsed. A few feet from the carriage into which her companions were helping her she saw Pushkin watching her with an intense expression in his blue eyes.

"Mademoiselle, your feet are wet," he murmured.

She did not answer and quickly got in; she thought it indecorous of him to have looked at her feet.

> *Well I remember waves in riot*
> *Before a storm; I wanted, too,*
> *Thus to rush forth, then lapse in quiet*
> *There at her feet, as they would do.*
> *The billows covered them with kisses,*
> *My lips were envious of their blisses!*
> *No, when with youth and love on fire,*
> *I did not ache with such desire*
> *To brush the shy lips of a maiden*
> *Or touch to flame a rosy cheek,*
> *Or with such urgent ardor seek*
> *To kiss the breast with languor laden;*
> *No, passion never wrought for me*
> *The same consuming agony.*[1]

[1]From *The Poems, Prose and Plays of Alexander Pushkin*, Copyright, 1936, by Random House, Inc.

Alexander returned to his carriage and called to the coachman to drive slowly. He felt the need to think. The image of Maria as he had just seen her—breathless, her hair in disorder, her eyes shining—would not leave him. For the first time he felt deeply moved by a woman's grace, moved to the point of pain. Until now his loves had been an excitement of the senses, the trembling of a heart avid to feel. He had flirted many times; he had never loved. But how was it possible to resist Maria?

Their being together was pure chance. He recollected the series of strange, unexpected events to which he owed his presence here in General Raevski's company, here with Maria. St. Petersburg, Kaverin, his parents, his mistresses— all that was both very near and very far away. The last months had been most difficult. The police were searching for his manuscripts. His father, who claimed to be sensitive and was really only cowardly, had turned away from a son in disgrace. His world had increased its sly attacks on his self-esteem. His appearance and his inconstancy had always earned him nicknames: "the Cricket," "the Spark." Now someone had invented a new one that was more malicious: "the Monkey."

The Emperor was furious. People said that Pushkin would be sent to Siberia or imprisoned in the Solovetski Monastery. Or again, which was worse, that the government did not take him seriously, that he was being treated like a naughty boy, that he had been conveyed to the offices of the secret police and whipped like a tramp to teach him a lesson. Remembering this infamous tattle, he could not help gritting his teeth, and his face lost its calm. These rumors were attributed to Count Tolstoi (known as "the American"), half adventurer, half man of the world; he had not even had time to challenge him to a duel. . . . But he would lose nothing by waiting.

He remembered his conversation with Miloradovich:

"Count, all my papers have been burned. But it is all here. Be good enough to give me some paper. . . ."

But Miloradovich was a gentleman, a soldier, the Russian Bayard, while the Czar was only an underhanded, revengeful man and Arakcheev's friend. Under the pretense of sending him South to serve the inspector general of colonists, the Czar was banishing him from St. Petersburg.

He had reached Ekaterinoslav, General Inzov's residence, still stupefied by his disgrace; he had half killed the post horses. After St. Petersburg, the dirty, lifeless, straggling town seemed as confining as a coffin. It was a provincial city, which in winter slept under snow and in spring under mud. A two-story house was a curiosity. The arrival of a stranger, a poet, a Pushkin, turned the whole place upside down for several days. It was almost as interesting as the fair.

As for Pushkin, the sight of this flock of low houses set him yawning. One evening he was eating oysters and drinking white wine in the only inn in Ekaterinoslav when two young men came in and sat opposite him. He asked them why they were staring at him.

"We have come to see Pushkin," they said in chorus.

He sighed. Such a degree of stupidity disarmed him.

"Very well, have you seen him? Now you can go. Good-by," he said, scraping an oyster shell. It was in such a place that he might have to spend several years.

He passed his days scribbling, biting his nails. The immense boredom of a Russian province weighed on him almost physically. Only nature, the wide, tumultuous

Dnieper, rested him from men. He could not resist the call
of its waters, barely freed from their winter ice. A week
later Nicholas Raevski, on his way through Ekaterinoslav,
had found him ill and completely abandoned, lying in the
wretched hovel of a Jew who did not dare to enter his room
for fear of contagion. Nicholas was going to the mineral
springs in the Caucasus with his father and his younger
sisters, Maria and Sophia. They had decided to take Pushkin
with them.

It was a week since Nicholas had arrived and had wrung
tears of joy from Pushkin by appearing unexpectedly in
his miserable lodging. He did not yet know whether to
curse or to bless the chance that had made him acquainted
with Maria.

ii

Gradually the flat green steppe had disappeared, giving
place to the first foothills of the Caucasus. The roads were
sheer and narrow and without parapets. The carriages made
their way slowly along a ribbon of roadway between a wall
and a precipice. Far off, the sharp profile of the highest
mountains in Europe traced a delicate white lacework
against the sky.

The district, which the Russians had only recently pacified, was dangerous to travel through, infested by unsub-
dued tribes—Chechens, Circassians—who attacked travelers,
drove off cattle, pillaged, took prisoners. . . . They were
proud mountaineers, so handsome that in spite of their

savage customs they were regarded as the most perfect representatives of the white race. Woe to the Russians who fell into their hands!

The party traveled under the protection of sixty Cossacks, armed to the teeth, always on horseback, always ready to fight, dragging along a cannon with a lighted fuse that was never allowed to go out. The shadow of danger was a delight to romantic imaginations fed on Richardson, Byron, and Rousseau. Brigands? Why, it was almost like something in Schiller!

Finally they reached their destination. The smoking springs poured down from the mountains, leaving rust-colored marks on the bare rock. Nothing grew in this land of subterranean fires, whose soil was constantly wet with boiling water and shaken by internal convulsions. Arid and grandiose, the landscape seized the imagination with a sacred terror.

There was not enough of anything—furniture, linen, dishes. They drew the mineral water directly from the springs in broken bottles, burning their fingers. Improvised bathtubs had been set up in tents.

It was the year 1820, when the world was in love with ruins and moonlight and melancholy music and violent romances. High stocks were in fashion, and Byron was the rage. Every little chinovnik at thirty rubles a month wore his heart on his sleeve and thought himself a Manfred, a Childe Harold, a child of the century. There were those who believed that they were disillusioned. There were those who really were so. Such a one was Alexander Raevski, the general's elder son, whom they had joined at the springs. Pushkin liked to listen to the bony young man, whose eyes were yellow, like a snake's. He found a strange pleasure in submitting the most sacred principles, the most firmly established ideas to the murderous analysis of Raevski's cold and bitter intellect. He enjoyed his atrabilious comments, which dissected the world as though it were a corpse, laying bare the miserable bones of things.

His corrosive logic attacked everything like an acid. Love? A trick of nature's to assure the continuation of the species, culminating in a grotesque and indecent gesture. Women? A rather damp lodging that a man must spend nine months in before he can enter the world.

Sometimes it seemed that the world crumbled away under the sapping blows of his terrible cynicism. But Alexander would always return to his demonic friend, as if he felt a need to pass through the cynical school. Yet, when they talked together at night, he put out the candles to escape his yellow snake's eyes.

Then he became the turbulent Pushkin again, the page, the curly-haired student, and wandered over the countryside armed with a heavy stick, at the risk of receiving a charge of shot in his chest. His head was full of rhymes, of poetic visions, of plans, of projects. Songs crowded into his mind and poured from his lips. It was there, on the roof of Europe, that he was at last to accomplish great things.

The grandly romantic landscape was full of memories of classic antiquity. It was on these sharp peaks, draped with forests and snow, that Prometheus had expiated his love of mankind. It was here that the Greek world had ended. Perhaps on his walks he passed the spot where Mithridates had committed suicide.

Thus, leaving Byron behind, he evoked Racine. But his magnetized mind kept returning to the dark girl whom he loved with a love that was incomplete and torturing and who would not believe it. He, the African, the man who was driven almost out of his senses by mere contact with a beloved woman, must resign himself to a tranquil friendship that permitted a touch, a look, the pressure of a hand. . . . His jealous and unhappy love made him timid and at a loss for words. He was no longer the insolent page, the curly-haired cherub he had been in St. Petersburg, the intimate of actresses and great ladies; he was a boy wildly in love, who thought in rhyme and passed the nights at his window.

iii

September was ending in a golden haze. For three weeks now they had been living in this fantastic, low, badly built château, all of whose doors gave on to the same corridor. It was at Gurzuf in the Crimea, a country of sun and grapes, lying against a red-brown mountain and all stuck with yews as straight as candles. The garden of their curious white house ran down to the narrow ribbon of beach bordered with foam. It was full of southern plants, a warlike flora bristling with spines and thorns, whose very flowers looked like maces—the dark, thick, lustrous vegetation of a rainless country. There was a cypress tree of which Alexander was particularly fond. He had always been subject to sudden friendships for trees.

The Raevskis had found the remaining members of the family at Gurzuf: the general's wife and his two elder daughters, Catherine and Helen. Catherine was a true soldier's daughter, beautiful, intelligent, and willful. Helen was the prettiest of the four sisters. She was dying of consumption. There was something touching, something angelic, in her beauty. She loved to go to balls and sit in a corner, so airy in her white dress that you feared she would fly away. Alexander was a little in love with them both, or rather, he was in love with the entire heroic and charming family. A family . . . It was something he had never had. . . . He thought of St. Petersburg, Sergei Lvovich, his bad verses and his avarice, "the beautiful Creole" who was no longer beautiful, and the whole cold, dilapidated house where nothing was where it belonged, neither things nor people.

Catherine . . . Helen . . . Maria . . . Their white skirts floated through the garden and through his dreams. Catherine was teaching him English from a collection of Byron's poems. How well the expressions of love became her beautiful firm mouth. But Maria, Maria with her brown shoulders and her soft, shortsighted eyes! Her friendship tormented him. She did not avoid him, but neither did she seek him out.

He was happy. He often bathed in the violet sea, cutting the heavy salt water strongly with his thin, muscular arms. Coming out, he would sit down and dry his hair, which the water had straightened, and eat grapes: yellow muscats which the country people had been harvesting for two weeks.

He made excursions up the red-brown mountain, clinging to his strong, steady little Tatar horse, which climbed straight up the steepest trails like a goat. But his eyes dwelt on the prints of a narrow little foot, which he had seen leaping impetuously before the sea. . . .

They went to visit the temple of Artemis, where Iphigenia landed in Aulis. Alexander gazed feelingly upon its Grecian marbles, fallen and broken, but touching because of all the recollections they contained. . . . When it was time to return, with their shoes full of pebbles they climbed laughingly into the carriages, which had been left at the foot of the mountain.

Alexander raised his eyes and saw Maria. She was sitting on a bench facing the sea with her back to him. He could see her smooth neck emerging from a ruffled collar, and the gold clasp of a *sautoir* from which hung a cross that, according to Orthodox custom, she never took off. He ran downstairs, forgetting his hat and stick.

He called, "Mademoiselle!"

She turned and smiled. The wide brim of her straw bonnet cast a delicate lacework of shadow flecked with sunlight on the upper half of her face. Her low-necked dress revealed her pure shoulders; they were rather thin, as such a young girl's ought to be. She did nothing to make herself look pale or to round out her fragile breast. There was nothing of affectation, nothing of coquetry, in her pose. She looked at him, smiling and swinging her arms, and that was all.

He stuttered: "I did not want to leave without telling you how much——"

She interrupted him: "Leave?"

"Yes, alas, it is time for me to think of going. General Inzov's offices have been transferred to Kishinev. I must join him there within a few days. But first I wanted you to know that the three weeks I have spent here have been the happiest in my life. And it is to you that I owe it. . . ."

He sat down beside her. She did not move away, but she stiffened.

"Come, come, Pushkin, you were certainly saying the same thing to my sister Catherine yesterday when you walked on the beach with her."

How happy he would have felt if there had been the least trace of jealousy in her words. But could a girl be jealous of a man she did not love? He answered angrily:

"Of course not, you know very well that Catherine Nikolaevna is giving me English lessons."

"English lessons at ten o'clock on a moonlight night like yesterday, and by the sea?"

"Why not?"

"And what is it, pray, that you do in the early morning under my sister Helen's window?"

"Pick up scraps of paper. She translates Byron and Walter Scott into French, but she tears up her translations and throws them out the window. I think it a shame because her translations are faithful and full of poetry."

"Good heavens, I did not know you were such a zealous student. With Catherine it's lessons; with Helen it's translations——"

He stopped her, calling her by her Christian name for the first time. "Don't joke, Maria." He took the little hand that tried to escape him and carried it to his lips. "You know very well that you are the only one. The others do not count, have never counted. Ah, Maria, if you would . . ."

She had at last succeeded in freeing her hand and said very low and fast: "Why did you want to spoil our friendship? You do not love and you will never love anything but your muse. I admire your verses—you know that—and I love you as I love my brothers. But for myself, I dream of a different destiny."

She rose, touched Alexander's forehead with her lips, and left him. He followed the white figure with his eyes until it disappeared around a turn. So the only woman who did nothing to make herself loved and whom no one could help adoring had refused him, would not listen to the words of love that were pressing to his lips. . . .

He sank his head and wept with humiliation, anger, and love. When he rose he had made up his mind. He would leave at once. He would fly from this too lovely and too luminous place. Since he could not devote his life to love, he would devote it to fame and adventures. If he could not be Lovelace he would be Don Juan and take his revenge upon all women for the wound he had received from one.

iv

Kishinev, annexed barely ten years earlier, was a strange city—part Moldavian, part Greek, part Russian, part Jewish, with a little Tatar thrown in. It was an oriental city—low, dirty, and picturesque. In its muddy streets, which were so narrow that you could not stretch your arms out without touching the two opposite walls, swarmed a ragged, alms-begging, noisy populace. Merchants caught passers-by by the arm and dragged them forcibly into their shops.

The Greco-Romanian aristocracy—the Zemfirakis, the Varfolomeis, the Inglezis—sat in their houses cross-legged, drank thick Turkish coffee, ate sweet and greasy confections, halva and rahat-loukoum, and conversed in bad French (which language had been introduced by the Russians). The ladies, who before the annexation had worn veils, now subscribed to fashion magazines and drank vinegar to make themselves look pale.

The city was flooded with Greek refugees who were fleeing from Turkish rule. The Russian officers—attired in varnished boots, tight trousers, gold-braided and fur-trimmed jackets thrown negligently over one shoulder—dragged their sabers through the cafés, the ballrooms, the streets, the casino.

Alexander was bored. At first the verminous exoticism of the strange city had interested him, then amused him, then wearied him. His brilliant friends in St. Petersburg had forgotten him. During the two years he had been in exile he had not received ten lines from them. In short, his relations with them had never been anything but that of a poetic parasite. There were still the faithful: Zhukovski, Karamzin, Vyazemski. They were trying to get him transfered to Odessa—a little Paris where at least there were buildings more than one story high, an Italian opera house, women of the world, and the sea.

St. Petersburg . . . The magical name awakened a cutting regret. St. Petersburg . . . It meant lights, the ballet, a whole turbulent life, a flavor of all Europe which he had only begun to taste.

He pretended to be disillusioned, but he was only soured and desperate. His life was beginning badly. At twenty-two, and marked by genius, he was dying of boredom and misery in a hole of a provincial city, without friends, without love, without money, without hope. The government hated him and surrounded him with spies. His fame was growing but not his income. The papers were glad to publish his poems but did not pay for them. The first chapters of his two new narrative poems, *The Prisoner of the Caucasus* and *The Bakhchisarai Fountain,* were circulating in hundreds of copies, written out by hand. His work was learned by heart, but it was not bought. He was the enchanter, Russia's first love. . . . Meanwhile, he had not money enough to order a new coat.

The government paid him seven hundred rubles a year, which he lost at the gaming table in two weeks. His father sent him letters expressing a paternal affection imbibed from the best authors but silently ignored his demands for funds. Alexander wrote to his brother: "I cannot live without *his* money. To live by my pen is impossible with the present censorship. As to carpentry, I was never taught it."

His lodgings, thanks to the kindly Inzov, cost him nothing; they were on the ground floor of a large empty house whose walls had been cracked by an earthquake. Inzov was rumored to be the illegitimate son of the Emperor Paul— the same Emperor Paul who had knocked Alexander's cap off with a riding crop when he was a little boy. Indeed, Inzov's resemblance to the late Czar was striking. Thus did the son make up for the sins of the father. Inzov liked his unruly subordinate, defended him to the authorities, and arranged his duels. But he was not rich, and Alexander was terribly in need of money.

He worked late and practiced shooting sitting on his bed, naked to the waist. The walls of his room were peppered with little holes, as if they had received a burst of grapeshot. At twenty paces he could send a bullet through the heart of a rose. He was feared, for he was known to be an excellent shot and quick to issue a challenge.

In the morning he liked to work in bed on a valise; into it he stuffed his papers, which were covered with fine, swift writing, full of blots and little drawings as keen and dry and nervous as his style. He gnawed the frayed end of his goose quill; his mobile face grew thoughtful and gentle. When he wrote, one could see the muscles working in his thin, bare arm.

His art was growing harsher and more virile. It was no longer the charming playfulness of *Ruslan and Ludmila,* in which his genius had toyed with recollections of Ariosto, Voltaire, and Parny. He sided resolutely with the moderns against the ancients, with the Romantics against the Classicists. But his verses remained supple, clear, light, and brilliant as spun glass. In the fire of his genius his mother tongue—hardly formed as yet, still full of dross, of clumsy expressions, of Slavisms—became as pure and precise as a diamond. Even in changing his allegiance he remained true to his masters, the French Classicists. He was a good artisan of letters soaked in Boileau, and he spent hours chiseling a stanza. When the work left his hands no trace of effort remained in the airy texture of his verses.

He was mad about Byron, the romantic, the shadowy, noble like himself and, like himself, cast out by society. The signs of this craze were visible everywhere. Like Byron, he despised the human race and wore soft collars. Like Byron, he was not averse to eccentricity. He appeared now as a Turk, now as a Jew. His dress usually consisted of a pair of velvet trousers and a cape, a costume which looked strange even in Kishinev. People came in from the surrounding countryside to see Mr. Pushkin in his red fez and his orange boots. But behind all this pose there was a misery that dared not tell its name. Pushkin looked as if he were protesting against the established order. As a matter of fact, he did not have money to pay a tailor.

The hero of his new poem, *The Prisoner of the Caucasus,* was a disillusioned man like Manfred. And the young Circassian girl, his first full-length portrait of a woman, had the black eyes, the heavy hair, and the brown shoulders of Maria Raevski. Zemfira, the heroine of *The Bakhchisarai Fountain,* a legend he had heard in the Caucasus and was putting into verse, also had eyes

> . . . *brighter than day,*
> *Darker than night.*

Maria, Maria . . . Her memory haunted him still after more than two years. The heroes of his poems were all created in his own image—men whose hearts bore the incurable wound of an unsatisfied love. Such was the "prisoner of the Caucasus," such the amorous khan of the *Fountain.*

It was she whom he sought in all women. . . . His official mistress was Calypso Polychroni, a Greek refugee with black eyes and curly hair. She lived in poverty with her mother, who told fortunes by cards, read coffee grounds, and went into trances for ten rubles. Calypso was short and spare, with a boyish figure and almost no breasts. She was beautiful, in spite of a large hooked nose, and wore a great deal of paint, like all oriental women. She was fond of singing Turkish ballads half aloud, accompanying herself on the guitar.

Alexander liked the poetic atmosphere that surrounded her: she was passionate and mysterious; she let men enter her bed for money and dreamed of becoming a nun. Calypso had learned to know love in the arms of Lord Byron. Pushkin adored in her the woman who had shared the couch of the greatest of English poets.

There was also Pulcheria Varfolomei, the daughter of a rich Moldavian gentleman, a plump, pretty doll, so soft and indifferent-seeming that her father had not been able to marry her off in spite of his great wealth. She looked like the allegorical figures that decorated the ceiling of the ballroom in which, twice a week, her father gave a ball. The chandelier hung directly from the breast of one of the figures, and Alexander amused himself by imagining that Pulcheria must have full pink breasts like that too. At times she seemed no more alive than a big wax doll. To his wit and his teasing she invariably answered in bad French:

"Ah, what a creature you is, Monsieur Pushkin! What is this jokes?"

Who else? Mariola Zemfiraki, Maria Eichfeld, Anika Sandulaki, Viktoria Vakar, Maria Balsh—whose husband he had slapped—and their daughter, a girl of thirteen. . . . He was filled with a dark compulsion to love. He tossed his heart to the firstcomer, provided she was good to look at. When he saw a pretty girl at her window he would climb to her balcony right from the back of his horse.

Secret reports regularly took the road to St. Petersburg. Mr. Pushkin behaves badly. Mr. Pushkin frequently fights duels. Mr. Pushkin publicly insults the army, the police, the government.

But Mr. Pushkin cared as little for his life as he did for his heart. He would fight a duel for a yes or a no. With Zubov, because he played cards badly. With Starov, because he had stopped him from dancing a mazurka. With Orlov, because he had called him a schoolboy. He carried the coquetry of courage to the point of going onto the dueling ground with cherries in his hat and continuing to eat them tranquilly under his opponent's fire. His dream was to go and fight for liberty in Greece. It was said that Lord Byron intended to do the same.

Kishinev was full of echoes of the Greek insurrection. Refugees flowed in and brought tales of Turkish atrocities. There was passionate discussion of the chances of the Hetaeria, who had attacked the ferocious power of the Ottomans without arms, without ships, rich only in their resolve to die for liberty.

All eyes were turned to the ancient land of the Greeks, the first, after France, to raise the banner of liberty. People waited impatiently for the Czar, who posed as the defender of the Slav peoples, to act, but the Russian government did not want the Orthodox Greeks to be victorious over the infidel Turks. The Sultan's soldiers had killed the old patriarch Gregory, robed in his sacerdotal garments, in a public square. The Most Christian Czar had not budged, because, Orthodox though they might be, the Greeks were nonetheless insurgents, lovers of liberty, revolutionaries. On their banner was inscribed the hateful word that was forbidden in Russia, the word whose mere sound made the czarist bureaucracy tremble: *Liberty!*

In this stifling atmosphere Alexander felt himself a prisoner. He could come and go like a free man, but he sensed around him the bars of an invisible cell. He was spied on. The police collected his sallies, made notes on his angry outbursts.

But police and conspiracy are the two sides of one medal. Tyranny implies revolt. About 1820 no one in Russia could say good morning to a friend without seeming a revolutionary and without really being one. Conspiracy was everywhere. The existence of a secret society whose aims were to abolish serfdom and establish either a constitutional monarchy or a democratic republic was no secret to anyone.

Pushkin breathed the air of conspiracy. His best friends belonged to the Union of Virtue, but the doors of the society remained closed to him. The conspirators were afraid of his impetuosity, even of his fame. Poets themselves, they wanted to preserve for Russia her greatest writer.

He was irritated by their refusal. Why might he not risk his life for a noble cause, when he was constantly exposing it in futile duels? He reacted violently. On the margins of his manuscripts his nervous pen was forever drawing little devils, horns, cloven feet, women displaying themselves, skeletons. It was his answer to the bigotry of the court, to the assumed air of virtue which the hypocritical Czar had brought into fashion.

He secretly composed a sacrilegious poem, the *Gabrieliad*, in which the myth of the Immaculate Conception was represented with a licentious realism that left *La Pucelle* and *La Guerre des Dieux* far behind. The Virgin was a loose woman, God a lascivious Jupiter, and the angel Gabriel a celestial procurer.

He seemed possessed by a demon that drove him always to show himself other and worse than he really was. He pushed his libertinism to the point of obscenity, his insolence to the point of rudeness, and his courage to the point of swagger.

He often thought of Ovid, who had died of boredom eighteen hundred years before, an exile in the very place where he himself was drowning his regrets for his wasted youth in wine and passionate excesses.

V

Count Vorontsov, governor general of New Russia
(capital: Odessa), had shut himself up in his office and
given orders that he was not to be disturbed. A terrified
silence had immediately descended on the house. The
count never became angry, never raised his voice, never
struck his orderlies; nevertheless, he was feared.

His Excellency sat before a large mahogany desk trimmed with bronze. Everything around him bore the marks of
a discreet and well-bred luxury. He liked paintings by the
masters, black marble busts, heavy draperies that fell in
rounded folds like columns. A member of a very wealthy
family, after his marriage with the Polish Countess Elisabeth Bronitska he had become one of the richest men in
Russia. His wife would say, "I believe I have twenty-eight
million rubles."

He laid down his quill pen and leaned back. His strong,
regular features took on the morose expression that was
natural to them under his mask of amiability and kindliness.
The terms of his report must be carefully considered. For
the second time he was writing to St. Petersburg in the
hope of getting rid of Pushkin. Hatred waked in him at
the mere sound of the name. But after all, who was this
Pushkin? A penniless beggar, a ne'er-do-well, in short, a
chinovnik at fifty-two rubles a month. Men like that—the
count had thousands of them at his beck and call. Yet when
Pushkin had arrived in Odessa, Vorontsov had received him

amiably—a little condescendingly, to be sure, but amiably. He had even invited him to his house and introduced him to his wife—he, the rich Vorontsov, the powerful Vorontsov, the ranking official of New Russia.

Pushkin had friends who stood well at court—Zhukovski, Karamzin, men of letters like himself (for Vorontsov, "man of letters" was nearly synonymous with "jailbird") who, it was known, had the Emperor's ear.

Pushkin suffered from the disease that afflicted every official: he was a poet. A fine state of affairs! To begin with, the count did not like this new school, the Romantics. A fashion, simply a fashion, which would not last two years. He liked five-act tragedies in verse and approved of the rule of the three unities. It would come back. And then, between a great poet and a great nobleman there was, after all, the devil of a difference. Corneille waited in the Prince de Condé's antechamber and dedicated his odes to financiers. And he was Corneille! Whereas this good-for-nothing of a Pushkin permitted himself to compose epigrams on him, Vorontsov, the governor of New Russia. He searched his memory:

> Half hero and half ignoramus,
> What's more, half scoundrel, don't forget.
> But on this score the man gives promise
> That he will make a whole one yet.

It was he who had inaugurated the silly fashion of pronouncing his name Worontsov, to ridicule the count's admiration for everything British. Besides, what was he paid his salary for? To work or to write verses? He spent his time taking sea baths and carousing on credit. He was seen everywhere—at the Turkish Café, at Othon's Restaurant, at the casino, at the opera (where they sang Rossini), but never at his desk. . . . He hobnobbed with suspicious characters—one Morali, or Moor Ali, an Arabian ex-pirate who wore oriental clothes and of whom Pushkin said: "I feel drawn toward him. His ancestors and mine may have been related." He had been seen sitting on the lap of this figure out of a comic opera, drinking champagne in his shirt sleeves. It was not the sort of thing a *gentleman* would do.

Yet he, Vorontsov, had given him an opportunity to make himself useful. He had sent him to combat the locusts that were devastating the Southern provinces, but Pushkin had come back in a week with an epigram:

> *Locusts, too tired to fly,*
> *Dropped from the sky,*
> *Ate everything,*
> *And then again took wing.*

This was the only result of his mission.

He, Vorontsov, was a serious man. Ever since he had succeeded the incapable Inzov, New Russia had known prosperity. He was having a road built along the coast. He had introduced grape growing into the province, and it had been a great success. Odessa, his capital, was a live European city, full of mercantile activity, with an Italian opera house and French restaurants. He was considering having the streets paved. Other governors took bribes and pillaged the provinces entrusted to their direction. *He* thought of nothing but winning distinction. He was severe, energetic, upright, at once a nobleman and a statesman, and a perfect gentleman to boot. He had no use for a Pushkin. He picked up his goose quill and wrote in French:

There are many people here—and their number will increase when the season for sea baths arrives—who, being passionate admirers of his poetry, try to show their friendship for him by excessive praises and thereby do him a bad service, for they increase his already high opinion of himself and make him believe that he is an excellent writer, whereas he is only a weak imitator of a highly undesirable original—Lord Byron—and whereas only work and an intense study of the great classic poets could bring to fruit the happy gifts of nature that it is impossible to deny him.

He smiled maliciously into his cravat. The formula was not bad. Everyone knew that Alexander I hated Byron. The insolent poet belabored him with sarcasms in his political poems. But what was there to do? One couldn't send Byron to Siberia or shut him up in a monastery or even banish him like Pushkin.

To recall Pushkin's admiration for Byron would be to revive the Emperor's antipathy. . . . He sanded the sheet with its official letterhead, folded it, and rang.

"Is the countess at home?" he asked the footman who opened the door.

"Yes, Your Excellency."

He rose, buttoned his long official frock coat, and glanced at himself in the mirror: he was no longer the brilliant officer he had been when he first knew Elisabeth. When the Russians entered Paris he had been in command of the troops that were to occupy the city. The Cossacks had camped on the Champs Elysées, and the Parisian ladies were astonished to hear the Russian officers speak French without a trace of accent.

Now he was a high official, a statesman. But women preferred uniforms. He passed through the long suite of staterooms, furnished in white and gold in the purest Louis XV style, and entered without knocking.

"*Comment allez-vous*, my dear?" he said, kissing his wife's hand. Vorontsov liked to speak English at home, but the habit of speaking French was too strong. The result was a mixture—which, as it happened, was highly fashionable.

Elisabeth had returned to her needlework. She was over thirty. At her age other women were old, but she was still beautiful and charming. Her profile suggested the Bourbons. Her quick glance—her eyes were not large, but they were an intense blue—seemed to caress whatever it touched. Her smile was irresistible. She had to the full that Polish charm that at once attracts and irritates.

He looked at her bowed neck with its smooth skin and little blond curls and sighed. Their marriage of money had at first been a marriage of love. That was all long ago. He knew that his wife was unfaithful to him, and he himself had mistresses. Rumor said specifically that she was conferring her favors on Alexander Raevski, the general's elder son, and even on Pushkin—but that idea was intolerable to him.

He cleared his throat and said:

"By the way—hmm. I have good news to tell you. What do you think? We shall soon be rid of our—Monsieur Pushkin." He watched her carefully. She had not moved; only, when he spoke the name, her needle had stopped short on its way through the canvas. He put his hand to his left side. These days, whenever he felt himself crossed, his heart beat in a way that worried him.

So it was true—Elisabeth, his wife, the mother of their little girl, preferred this rhymester to him, this wild man who did not even know English and who pronounced "time," "dear," and "Byron" as they were spelled!

"Well, have you nothing to say to that?" he asked angrily.

"What do you wish me to say, *mon ami?*" the young woman answered quietly. He thought, "How well she controls herself!"

"Excuse me," he muttered. "I have work to do," and he left the room almost at a run—he who was always careful to walk majestically, with a certain stiffness, as he had seen the peers walk in the House of Lords in London.

Elisabeth followed him with her eyes. How vanity had changed him! It angered him to see that she no longer admired him unreservedly, as once she had. But she was older, and he was no longer the just and clearheaded man she had known. Now he looked for compliments from his subordinates, almost demanded them. . . .

She sighed. The long embroidery needle sped through the canvas once more. She worked with her head bent very low. For some time her sight had been growing weak. She was no longer a young woman, yet she could still please and she liked to please. Sometimes, at intimate moments, when he was not thinking of playing the part of a perfect gentleman, her husband reproached her for the lovers with whom gossip credited her. Raevski, melancholy, sarcastic, and cutting, had a passion for her so extravagant that it frightened her. But Pushkin was different. . . .

Their relations had begun badly. She had spent the summer at the mineral springs. By the time she returned to Odessa, Pushkin had been there for some time under Count Vorontsov's orders. Like many women of the world, she was interested in literature. She wanted to know the author of *Ruslan* and *The Prisoner of the Caucasus*.

He was introduced; she saw a thin young man with the profile of an Arab, thick-lipped, who burst out laughing and showed his perfect teeth. He had a slender waist, tousled hair, and small hands. He pleased her and irritated her.

Once at a reception she asked a friend:

"What is being given at the theater today?"

Pushkin, who was present, turned quickly and, putting his hand over his heart, as he always did when he was going to be impertinent, bowed and answered:

"*La Spòsa Fidele,* Contessa!"

She could have struck him.

He was said to be the lover of Mrs. Riznich, an eccentric woman who wore top hats and skirts so long that they dragged on the ground, doubtless to hide her feet, which were extremely large. She was said to be very beautiful and ardent. Did she not have Jewish blood in her veins? Elisabeth did not know her. Their spheres did not touch. Countess Vorontsov was a great lady; Mrs. Riznich, after all, was only the wife of a rich merchant who dealt in grain. However, they were rivals. When the gilded youth of Odessa left the Vorontsovs' luxurious palace they went to supper at Mrs. Riznich's, where no outsiders were invited. Without admitting it to herself, Elisabeth was a little jealous. Did she want to steal a lover from a woman who— she had heard—was younger and more beautiful than herself? The fact remains that she always treated Pushkin with the exquisite and almost imperceptible coquetry that had turned heads far harder than a poet's.

She had not found it very difficult. For several months now Pushkin had been at her feet. Amaliya Riznich had departed to Italy, which was her birthplace. Rumor said that she was dying of consumption, that her husband and her lovers had abandoned her. . . . Alexander had confessed to Elisabeth the torturing passion that this woman of the South had aroused in him. His heart—the weak heart of a man and an artist—had emerged, lacerated but stronger, from the abysses of a devouring jealousy. The sensual storm was over, and in the fire of that fiendish love the image of a dark, indifferent child-woman had died.

Now he was forgetting the vampire in Elisabeth's white arms. Her Polish sweetness inspired him to tender poems full of music. So in his turbulent heart, eager to live and avid to feel, one love drove out another.

Elisabeth straightened up. Her reverie had carried her far from her perfumed boudoir. She remembered her husband's words: "Good news . . . rid of Pushkin . . ." So he knew everything and had revenged himself basely and underhandedly by sending a secret report to St. Petersburg.

But in that case Alexander was in danger. He must be warned. She sat down at her desk, hurriedly wrote a few words, then she rang.

"Take this to Monsieur Pushkin," she said to the chambermaid, "and make sure that no one sees you!"

vi

On July 30, 1824, a young man wrapped in a long black cape and wearing a red fez entered the smoky parlor of the only inn in Mogilev. In a corner a group of young men who were waiting for post horses were killing time playing cards and drinking bad white wine.

Outside a mauve twilight was enveloping the little town, stifled in dusty foliage. It was hot. Big black flies zigzagged back and forth and bumped against the windowpanes, buzzing. The air was heavy with the laziness, the inertia, the age-old dilatoriness of provincial Russia.

The young man took off his cape, without laying down the heavy stick he carried, and looked threateningly at the occupants of the room, who were staring superciliously at his wide trousers and his fez. Suddenly one of them rose hastily.

"Pushkin! Why, it's Pushkin!" He turned to his companions. "Gentlemen, you have the honor to be contemplating the greatest poet the soil of Russia has produced!" He seized the newcomer's hand. "Come, Pushkin, don't you recognize me? I'm Engelhardt's nephew—Engelhardt, the director of the lyceum of Tsarskoe Selo. Don't you remember? On Sundays you used to make me recite poetry."

"Ah, Sasha? Yes, now I remember. You were a fine fellow."

"You won't refuse to take something with us?"

"I'd be glad to. But I cannot stay very long. I am obliged to continue my journey."

"You won't have any horses before tomorrow morning. Between now and then we shall have plenty of time to talk. Waiter, champagne!"

The waiter brought several bottles. Engelhardt's nephew performed the introductions.

"Prince Obolenski, Nicholas Panaev, Mansurov. . . . Gentlemen, the prince of poets needs no introduction!"

"Would it be indiscreet to ask where you are bound?" asked Obolenski.

A shadow passed over the traveler's mobile face. "I have no reason to conceal it. I am returning to my father's house in the province of Pskov. Your health, gentlemen!"

The young men raised their foam-crowned glasses and emptied them.

"Your health!"

Pushkin seemed somber and preoccupied. He talked little and drank much. Little by little the wine reddened his sallow cheeks. He grew animated.

By ten o'clock they were all rather drunk and on terms of considerable intimacy. Night had fallen, bringing a certain frankness. The waiter brought candles and a fresh supply of champagne.

"So that scoundrel Vorontsov has had you banished from Odessa," said Mansurov, who had hiccups. "But why the devil didn't you challenge him to a duel?"

Pushkin smiled somberly. The wine had made him melancholy.

"A few years ago a fortuneteller told me that I should die by the hand of a blond man or by that—if I may put it so —of a white horse. Now Vorontsov is not only a blond man, he is also an animal. You can understand that I took precautions!"

"A sad age." Obolenski sighed. "The Czar dismisses Pushkin for misconduct and makes a count of Arakcheev, the filthiest scoundrel in the empire. *O tempora, O mores!*"

"Obolenski, you speak golden words!" cried Pushkin. "Why are you not always drunk?"

Obolenski, feeling flattered, went on: "Gentlemen, this day upon which the greatest Russian writer has crossed our path should be celebrated by some signal act. . . . What could we think up?" He struck his forehead. "I have it! Eureka! We'll give our poet a bath in champagne!"

Pushkin burst out laughing, throwing back his head.

"My friends, I thank you. I should be very glad to bathe in champagne. . . . Unfortunately I am in a hurry. Orders are orders." He took a paper from his pocket and read: " 'The Collegiate Assessor Pushkin will go directly to his parents' house in the province of Pskov, passing through Nikolaev, Elisavetgrad, Kremenchug, and not stopping anywhere.' You see, I must be off. What time is it?"

"Four in the morning."

Pushkin whistled. "Good-by, my friends."

The young men followed him out. Obolenski wrapped him in his cape and gave him his stick. Pushkin settled himself in the carriage and made a sign to the coachman. The man picked up the reins.

It was the hour of uncertain light that comes before dawn. The horizontal contours of the flat, monotonous countryside were defined in the east against a patch of green sky where the sun would rise. Cocks crowed in the distance, greeting the coming of day. Pushkin shivered and wrapped himself in his cape, rested his head against the back of the carriage, and shut his eyes. It was the end of July. The short Russian summer was almost over; the days were still hot, but the nights were already chilly. They were nearing the North. Soon he would find again the white trunks of birches, a sky swollen with clouds, yellowed gardens touched by autumn, all the melancholy landscape that he had not seen for four years.

The steady trotting of the horses dulled his thoughts and made him sleepy. Again he was on the road; again he was an exile. This time it was not the exotic South but the Northern countryside that awaited him—flat, monotonous, gray in summer, white in winter. . . . For how many years? He did not know.

It had all come so quickly, like a storm. The fact that he had been stricken from the list of officials of the Ministry of Foreign Affairs left him indifferent. His poems brought him income enough. Vyazemski, who had undertaken to publish *The Bakhchisarai Fountain,* had sent him three thousand rubles. Three thousand rubles! More than he had earned in four years in the Czar's service!

But now they were going to shut him up for several years in a forgotten village, on account of a stupid letter he had imprudently written to a friend in Moscow:

You want to know what I am doing? I am writing the brilliant stanzas of a romantic poem and taking lessons in pure atheism. There is an Englishman here, a deaf philosopher, the only intelligent atheist I have ever met. . . . The system is not as consoling as is generally supposed; but of them all, it is unfortunately the most likely to be true.

He had forgotten the methods of the Russian government. The police intercepted the letter. The pretext for which the authorities were waiting, in order that they might satisfy the illustrious Count Vorontsov, was ready to hand. "Atheism . . . system likely to be true . . . intelligent philosopher . . ." Why, it was enough to send a man to Siberia! The government contented itself—a signal mercy!—with exiling him to his parents' estate, Mikhailovskoe. After all, we are not barbarians!

He remembered Elisabeth's tears. The sweet creature

. . . When they parted she had given him a ring engraved with an inscription in Hebrew.

"It is a talisman," she had said, smiling. "It will not protect you from death, but it will guard you from love vows that do not come from the heart."

He disengaged his left hand and pressed his lips to the stone, which was covered with strange signs.

The red disk of the rising sun nicked the immense, pure sky, driving away the blue, cool darkness. In the growing light the carpet of grain undulated to infinity, lying down in waves under the morning wind.

Collegiate Assessor Pushkin, exiled for a few lines of a letter, slept in his post chaise, lulled by the dull, regular noise of eight hoofs on the road.

The Idyl

M Y ANGEL, WILL YOU change this towel?" groaned Sergei Lvovich. He lay, fully dressed, on his bed, his face covered with a cloth that dispensed a strong odor of vinegar. Sergei Lvovich was having a headache like a prima donna. It was the same thing every time his eldest son addressed a word to him.

Nadezhda came to her husband's bedside and put her hand on his forehead. "Calm yourself, my friend, I beg you," she said in French.

Sergei Lvovich took the succoring hand and printed a kiss upon it, for in spite of his sufferings he never forgot to be polite. Then he sank back with a groan that Mademoiselle Georges would have envied.

"We shall leave this house," he murmured in a dying voice. "My duty as a father demands that I remove our other children from the influence of that monster, that unnatural son. . . . " He raised his hands to his forehead, squeezed out a tear, showed every symptom of intense despair.

"We shall leave if you wish it, my friend," said Nadezhda in her colorless voice. "But calm yourself, in heaven's name!"

Sergei Lvovich was satisfied with seeing his wife really alarmed. He liked to be the center of concern. At the slightest indisposition he groaned, talked of dying, refused to see the doctor. He opened his eyes and murmured, "Where is he?"

"Who?"

"Alexander."

"He has gone riding."

Sergei Lvovich closed his eyes again, sighed—in short, behaved like a cruelly tried father. Tried he was! Yes, not only had he been obliged to receive an exiled son who brought disgrace upon the entire family and particularly upon him, Sergei Lvovich; but he had to put up with his silences, his cold looks, his reproaches. Yes, his reproaches, because Sergei Lvovich had advised Léon and Olga to stay away from the monster exiled for atheism.

No doubt Sergei Lvovich had been a roué himself, a freethinker, a freemason, but from that to being an atheist —and above all to admitting it in a letter—there was a considerable distance! In his day a man could be a Voltairian without quarreling with the government over it.

Yet to this unnatural son, to this convict, he had opened his arms when he had come to Mikhailovskoe and, as it were, killed the fatted calf in his honor. Figuratively speaking, of course, for Sergei Lvovich was far too economical to kill anything in honor of anybody. Yet to harbor a person whom the government regarded with such disfavor was not without its dangers. Alexander was kept under constant surveillance. The authorities had even proposed that he—Sergei Lvovich—should undertake that delicate matter himself. *He* was not a suspect, a banished man, an atheist, but an upright citizen, the father of a family.

He had accepted; he would watch over his son for his own good. Had he not the right—was it not his duty—to open his letters? Was that any reason for Alexander to burst into his room, cover him with reproaches, and give him a headache? Ah, children are ungrateful creatures!

Sergei Lvovich had not stayed for more. He had run out of the room; he had called for help; he had sobbed and shouted that his son had killed him, or at least struck him, or anyway wanted to strike him. Alexander had bowed, had taken his horse, and had been gone several hours.

October was ending in a white mist that lay like a scarf in the hollows. At night the wind howled in the chimneys of the old manor house, which dated from the days of the Moor. It swooped furiously down on the great trees in the park, which swayed and shook their yellowed crowns with a noise like chafed silk. The dead leaves, which no one cleared away, piled up on the walks, rotted in the pools of rain, giving off a fresh, bitter odor.

Over the gray sky the wind kept driving torn and fleeting clouds. It was a Russian autumn, the autumn of the Romantic poets, favorable to inspiration, to long night watches alone with a sheet of paper and that old and tried friend, the frayed quill pen. But Alexander's thoughts were elsewhere. Whatever brought to mind the sea saddened him; the sound of a fountain made him uneasy. A clear sky made him weep with rage. He had a fashionable illness, the spleen.

Sergei Lvovich had left for St. Petersburg, wrapped in his cape, his dignity, and his despair. The family had followed. Alexander had remained—together with his old nurse, his manuscripts, his regrets, his memories.

Mikhailovskoe was a wretched village, with no church, and the barin's house was a long, low wooden structure one story high, furnished with bric-a-brac and limping tables and one-armed armchairs and crippled beds. He slept on a divan, wrote on a card table, a jam pot served him for an inkwell. In that jam pot were born the purest masterpieces of Russian literature. The only rooms that were heated were his bedroom and the nyanya's bedroom, where the serf women spun.

The Russian countryside drowned this nest of gentlefolk in its wave. The woods were deep and quiet, like cathedrals. The region had been sculptured by glaciers, which had left it full of lakes, open to the sky like blue eyes. And everywhere there was a silence so pure that you listened to it as if it were music.

But Alexander had a ravenous appetite for liberty, for movement, for travel. Somewhere in the world were Paris, London, Italy. . . . There were theaters, factories, parliaments, cafés, museums, newspapers. "Pyroscaphic vessels," propelled by steam, crossed the ocean without the help of sails. In England there was another new invention, a kind of carriage called a "locomotive," which did not have to be pulled by horses. In Paris the streets were lighted by a kind of gas extracted from oil.

Here life flowed densely and slowly, as it had under Czar Peter, as it had under Ivan the Terrible. The serf, bent over the clodded soil, dragged himself along behind his wooden plow. The nobility danced, chattered French, read Rousseau, but picked the enslaved countryside clean. Ladies, raising their little fingers, talked of platonic love and the rights of passion; but when a chambermaid stole a handkerchief she was given fifty lashes from a whip made of braided leather, with its end dipped in glue, which tore her thighs open to the bone. Ah, he had had enough of Holy Russia! How gladly he would take his hat and stick and go to breathe the air of Europe!

He would wake late and work in bed, and then take an ice-cold bath and set off on horseback. The peasants took off their hats as he passed. He bowed his curly head. His horse's hoofs made a clear sound on the frost-hardened ground: *tak, tak, tak*. The branches touched his face like fingers as he rode through the hollow lanes along the interminable forest glades.

At three o'clock the sun—red as a frost-bitten nose—set in a mauve mist behind the shaggy pines. He would return. The interminable evening would begin. The old clock chimed the hours with a cough, and the wood crackled sharply in the fireplace. He would stare into the fire so long, humming an air of Rossini's, that he saw green flames everywhere.

The knitting needles moved in his old nyanya's wrinkled hands; her kerchief, knotted on top of her head, threw a horned shadow on the wall.

"Let's drink a toast, Mama," he would say to the old serf. She would bring two goblets and they would drink. Cheered, she would begin to tell some marvelous tale, just as she had done twenty years before, when she had held him—little and curly-headed and dressed in his long lace nightgown—against the breasts that now were shriveled.

How trivial and overdone Voltaire and Parny and even Byron seemed, compared with these tales of the people who were so simple, so colorful, so strong. Herder was right: there lay the true fountain of poetry. He stored his memory with his nyanya's songs and stories, with the legends of the district. He listened to beggars singing at the doors of churches. Wearing his shirt over his trousers like a muzhik, the elegant Pushkin mingled with the crowd on market days. One day a policeman, thunderstruck by such behavior, arrested the barin who was shaking hands with peasants.

Byron had died for liberty in Greece. Alexander had a Mass said for the repose of his soul, but inwardly he had freed himself of Byron as, five years earlier, he had outgrown Voltaire. On the table by his bed *Macbeth, King Lear, The Merry Wives of Windsor,* and *Hamlet* had replaced *Manfred* and *Childe Harold.*

Shakespeare—what a terrifying genius! Byron was poor stuff compared with the demiurge in whose works kings spoke like kings, soldiers like soldiers, women like women. Byron had conceived only one character—his own. He had given one of his characters his pride, another his hatred, a third his melancholy. Add them up, and the result was always Byron. Pushkin wrote:

"After Schackspire, my head whirls. . . . I feel as if I were looking into a black and terrifying abyss. . . ."

Emerging from the abyss, his brain on fire, he worked at his *Boris Godunov,* a tragedy in blank verse on a subject from Russian history, in which the neglect of the stifling rules of classic drama, the richness of the plot, the truth of the characters, and the poetry of the language were all Shakespearean and all Pushkin at his best.

His soul was like an overfull vase. At the least touch melodies overflowed and poured from his pen in brilliant verse. His *Gypsies,* a severe and pure narrative poem, was finished. Into it he had put his memories of a woman briefly loved, for whose sake he had spent several days on the road with a picturesque and tattered crowd of Bessarabian Romanies. Then, forgetting their walks hand in hand over the faded steppe, under a great low moon yellow as an owl's eye, his wild mistress had left him for another.

For a long time he had been trying to create the figure of a contemporary man, a typical child of the century, at once Pushkin, Chaadaev, and Raevski—cold and passionate, melancholy, elegant, disdainful, cynical. The "prisoner of the Caucasus" and the hero of *Gypsies* were sketches of the character that haunted him.

At Odessa he had begun a novel in verse and had felt that he had at last found his path. Eugene Onegin—such was the name of the Russian René. At his side, a being of crystalline purity and nobility, concealing under the sober exterior of a well-brought-up young provincial lady an ardent and generous soul—Tatyana. . . . It was a strange and charming poem, full of smiling and poetic digressions, of confessions that seemed to be murmured in whispers and in which the heroes of novels mingled with the living, like portraits coming down out of their frames in dreams. It was as if the author took you by the hand and led you on a long walk, stopping sometimes to catch a breath or to look at the sky, interrupting his story to evoke a sad memory, addressing the reader familiarly, like an old acquaintance.·

His language, his perfectly pure and chaste style had been enriched by contact with Shakespeare without losing anything of its exquisite nudity. Apollo, Jupiter, nymphs, cupids—all the old theatrical rubbish, all the old classical props that had been worn to shreds by poets ever since the Renaissance—had vanished from his stanzas. But his noble ordering of sentences—subject, verb, object; subject, verb, object—had remained severely Athenian. It was poetry in a pure state, cleansed of all earthly dust, and almost geometrical in its perfection.

He pushed open the door and entered the house. A little of the fog that was heavy outside entered with him.

"I've shot a duck," he said to the nurse. "Let it stay in the pantry for a few days. I want to have it high for Sunday." She took the duck and started for the pantry. "By the way," he called, "send Olga to me, will you?" and turned away too quickly.

He went to the window and pressed his forehead against the damp pane. Never anything but this dull white stopper of fog. . . . It took a miracle of faith to believe that there was a sun behind the low sky that fitted over the world like a potlid.

He yawned and went over to the mirror. He was still the same—thin, curly-haired, easily moved to bursts of laughter. The side whiskers that he had let grow in accordance with the dictates of fashion framed his pale cheeks. He wore his nails cut at an angle. The nail of his fifth finger was so long that he had to protect it with a little gold shield, a thing that stupefied the peasants.

Someone knocked timidly. He called:

"Come in!"

A girl half opened the door.

A few days earlier, having nothing better to do, he had gone into the room where the peasant women spun under the supervision of his nurse. A heavy odor of sweat stopped him on the threshold; the windows were shut, and ten women were working in the room.

The spinners had risen and bowed from the waist, as if they had been broken in two. They were big red-faced girls, with hair bleached by sun and wind and eyebrows that were almost invisible. He was on the point of leaving when suddenly his eyes fell on a bowed head, a soft neck with little blond curls. He stopped.

"What is your name?"

The girl raised her blue eyes; they were swimming with shyness. A purple wave spread over her neck, her cheeks, her forehead. For a peasant, she had a delicate complexion.

"Olga—her name is Olga, Alexander Sergeevich," the nurse answered and, looking at the girl severely: "Come, girl, have you been stricken dumb? Can't you answer the barin?"

Now again she stood before him, awkward in her tightly tied high-waisted peasant's apron, her arms hanging loose, her kerchief knotted under her pretty chin.

"Come, Olga, sit down, don't be afraid."

She sat down on the edge of the divan, her eyes obstinately lowered. Under her kerchief he saw the soft neck that had struck him and the heavy roots of a yellow braid, the color of straw and sunlight and honey. Her tight bodice naïvely outlined two breasts that were already heavy but which promised to be round and firm. She was breathing quickly and lightly, as if she were afraid to take a deep breath.

A woman . . . he looked at her as if he were surprised to find, under her peasant dress, the same softness, the same rounded forms, the same delicious and enervating mystery. He sat down beside her, took her hot and trembling hand—noticing that her fingers were rough from being pricked by her needle—and printed a kiss on it. A shudder ran through her big warm body. He gently murmured:

"Olga!"

For the first time she dared to raise her eyes and saw him close beside her, so gentle, so different, as if he belonged to another species.

She was sixteen. The sad destiny of Russian peasant women held a future for her that was without any mystery: always pregnant, doing hard labor under the July sun, her belly heavy, bringing forth under a millstone, like a mare. In ten years she would be an old woman. . . .

She looked furtively at the slight, elegant figure beside her. The boys who courted her in the village were big and red-faced, with dirty straw-colored hair and square hands. He was thin and pale, with black curly hair, polished nails, a red mouth. His tight coat outlined his hips femininely. He was a barin who could read and write and knew an unknown language and kissed her hand as he would a lady's. . . .

"Olga!"

No one had ever spoken to her in a voice like that, insinuating, full of caresses. She raised her eyes to him with an adoring look that was full of an animal submission, that forgave everything beforehand. He laid his hand on her warm, full breast—as her master, as her lover.

My dear Vyazemski, you hold your tongue, I hold my tongue, and we do well to hold our tongues. One day we shall talk at leisure. For the moment there is another matter in question.

This letter will be delivered to you by a very charming and very good girl whom one of your friends has imprudently made pregnant. I count on your humanity and your friendship. Find a refuge for her in Moscow, give her what money she needs, and afterward send her to Boldino (my patrimony, where there are hens, cocks, and bears). You can see that there is enough matter here for a whole missive in the style of Zhukovski, sur le pope. But there is no need for posterity to know our humanitarian exploits.

And now, with truly paternal tenderness, I ask you to look after the child if it should be a boy. I should not want to send him to an orphanage. Couldn't he be sent to the country, to Ostafevo, for example?

My friend, I feel ashamed, I assure you—but what has my shame to do with it! Farewell, my angel, are you ill or not? We are all ill with one sickness or another. . . . Answer in detail.

ii

"Annie, Annie, where are you? Pushkin is here!"

Annie flew to the mirror, puffed out the hair over her temples, took up a French novel, and half reclined on the sofa. He was to find her in that romantic posture, languid, half lying down, *La Princesse de Clèves* in her hand.

But he lingered in the garden. She heard his laugh and the voice of her sister Evpraksiya, called Zizi, a youngster of fourteen who was already coquetting. Annie tried to keep still, so that her curls would not come out, and felt a blush of emotion spread over her neck and her cheeks. As if she were not red enough already!

She was twenty-four and unmarried, with a round face and sad eyes. High-waisted dresses—they were said to be going out of fashion—outlined her too full breasts. She was sentimental and often cried over sad love stories. To become Pushkin's mistress would have been a joy to her, although people said he was having an affair with a serf girl.

Annie had allowed him to kiss her on the lips, to put his hand on her heavy warm breasts. A word would have been enough to bring her to Mikhailovskoe secretly, to share her poet's bed. But that word he did not speak.

Their kisses, the little innocent games from which they both emerged red and with their hair in disorder, were the small change of love which the world accepted, even excused. But she wanted to suffer for him and through him; she wanted to sacrifice herself entirely, to abandon herself completely.

At bottom she was perfectly aware that she was an object of indifference to him and that only his boredom had been responsible for the few minutes of attention which she guarded as a precious memory. Devotion, patience, tears, submission bored him. He liked women to be coquettish, witty, vivacious, and to desire to please him.

Zizi, little Zizi, that fourteen-year-old demon with her slim waist and budding breasts, pleased him much more with her repartees, her insolence, her babyish pouting. All the great poet's looks and words and flattering attention—and he was twenty-six—went to Zizi, while her grown-up sister was left disdainfully in a corner of the drawing room.

He was lingering in the garden with Zizi. . . . Presently they would have tea on the veranda, Zizi would make the punch, Netty—their cousin—would play Rossini, and she would remain silent in her corner, unhappy because she had not had her poet to herself for even a few minutes.

Useless to stay there on the faded sofa, pretending to read *La Princesse de Clèves*. From force of habit she glanced at herself in the mirror, and her face seemed to look fuller than ever. This fashion of puffing out one's hair over the temples—it was unbecoming to her.

If only she had more chances of catching his attention. But Trigorskoe, their estate, only a few versts from the Pushkins' domain, was the gathering place of all the young people in the neighborhood. And the young people were mostly girls—cousins, friends, relations. Their house, a big, rambling, one-story wooden building, was always full of soft voices, rustlings, laughter, whispering, light steps, the trailing of skirts. A veritable feminine kingdom. Nothing but Catherines, Annies, Marias, Natashas, Adeles, and Alexandras.

During vacations their brother Alexis, a student at Dorpat, would bring friends, poets. Then everything woke up. On summer evenings there were kisses in the park on the old mossy benches, or couples watched the tremulous reflection of the moon in the old fishpond, holding hands. In winter there were games—blindman's buff, paper chases, charades, musical chairs, "Fly, pigeon, fly." "What is my forfeit?" . . . "You shall kiss Alexandra three times on the lips."

Someone was always playing Rossini on the piano in the old, rather dark drawing room whose french windows gave on to the garden. Rossini had been brought in by Pushkin, who said that his music was as sweet as youthful kisses. Everything in the house evoked Pushkin: they recited his poems; they sang his ballads; they talked of him at night by their open windows in the rooms where two girls often shared a bed.

Annie had too many rivals: Evpraksiya, Netty, Cousin Praskovya, who was called Pauline. . . . They all had a claim on his homage. Her mother herself, whose maternal affection for her twenty-six-year-old neighbor concealed a deeper emotion, had not been able to resist his page's manners, his intelligent profile.

With the instinct of a jealous woman Annie watched her mother making the best of her matronly right to run her hand through Pushkin's black curls. There was more than the peaceful friendship of an older woman for a young man in Mrs. Ossipov's letters: "Son of my heart . . . I kiss those beautiful blue eyes of yours that I love so much. . . ."

She could hoodwink Zizi, Alexandra, or Pushkin himself, but she could not hoodwink Annie. Annie knew her mother loved Pushkin as only a woman of forty who has loved greatly can love a young man.

The grain—so high that it hid a standing man completely —bent softly under the warm wind. The silence was alive and full of sounds that made it perceptible: the dry noise of crickets in the grass, the chirping of birds, the rustle of leaves.

Alexander knew every stone of the road to Trigorskoe because he had traveled it almost every day for a year. For a year he had been buried here, exiled, forgotten by everyone. There were moments when he found his solitude sweet. But these months of enforced immobility had given him a raging appetite for liberty. To escape had become his one idea. Alexis Vulf—the son, by her first husband, of his neighbor Mrs. Ossipov—wanted to take him to Dorpat disguised as a serf body servant. Dorpat was almost out of the country; the frontier was only a step away. You went through Dorpat to go to Revel, where you took the boat for Stettin. . . .

His only visitors in his rustic prison had been good old Pushchin and Baron Delvig, his two best friends at the lyceum. Pushchin had brought three bottles of champagne and *The Misfortune of Being Intelligent,* a comedy that had just appeared and was turning the two capitals upside down.

As for the baron, who kissed his hand to show his admiration every time they met, he had spent a week at Mikhailovskoe, almost all of it in bed. He was lazy, with the Russian laziness that was born of centuries of immobility. Such people were frequently to be met with among the Russian nobility; they spent their lives in a dressing gown, dreaming on a divan, looking out the window, eating, growing fat. Laziness was like a rust that ate such natures to the heart. They ended by being too lazy to dress, to go out, to talk, and became the slaves of their own servants. . . .

Now Delvig was gone. Once again he was alone in the big, low house. He spent whole days at Trigorskoe, returning home only when he sensed rhymes coming and felt the need of solitude. Annie bored him with her passion, her tears, and her four-page letters. Sometimes he wished he could chase her away, as one chases away a fly whose buzzing becomes an obsession. Mrs. Ossipov herself was good and amusing, but at forty she did not yet consider herself an old woman. He wrote verses for her album, ringing the changes on St. Martin's summer and on autumn flowers that are sometimes lovelier than the flowers of spring. . . .

Only Zizi, who had just turned fifteen—an unripe fruit whose shoulders promised a brilliant maturity—occupied him, together with her cousin Netty. But all these flirtations without results left his mind and his heart empty. The memory of Elisabeth Vorontsov no longer troubled his sleepless nights. After all, his life was in the scribbled and blotted pages of *Boris Godunov*, of *Eugene Onegin*, of *Mozart and Salieri*, his new play.

In the distance he saw the long, low outline of Trigorskoe and walked faster. The voice of little Maria, Mrs. Ossipov's youngest daughter, called, "Here's Pushkin!"

Running up to him, she said, "Mother is in the drawing room; we have guests."

He entered, took off his hat, and bowed. Annie was pouring pale, smoking tea. Near the table he saw a woman whom he did not recognize. But where had he seen before that beautiful face?

"Anna," said Mrs. Ossipov, "let me introduce Pushkin. . . . We are fortunate enough to have him as a neighbor. My dear Pushkin, allow me to present my niece, Mrs. Kern."

He bowed silently, almost timidly, as always when he was really impressed. The young woman had yellow hair. She did not wear it puffed out at the temples as fashion decreed; it made a supple frame for her beautiful face and her gray eyes. Alexander's eyes passed quickly over a well-proportioned bust and wide hips under the full bell skirt that was in fashion. He listened: the tones of her voice were low and warm. She must sing well.

"We have met somewhere before, Monsieur Pushkin. I have it! It was at the Olenins', in St. Petersburg, five or six years ago. . . . I remember it perfectly; we were giving charades. . . ."

"And you played Cleopatra, madame. A role that became you."

He grew animated. His voice took on the persuasive tone that was one of his weapons of seduction and which acted almost physically on women's nerves. His desire to please her made him suddenly poetic and brilliant. She listened to him, leaning on one elbow, her chin in her hand. Her beautiful arm was bare almost to the shoulder. An uncertain smile flickered over her sensual lips which contrasted with the chaste light in her large gray eyes.

The others stopped talking, displeased to see their poet so captivated by an intruder. Finally he took his hat and left. He felt a need to reflect. Once again he was succumbing, a prey to love.

Anna remained where she was, dreaming, insensible to the pinpricks of her jealous cousins. Hers was a healthy and passionate nature, made for love and childbirth. The Emperor Alexander, who had danced with her during a progress through the provinces, had compared her with Queen Louise.

At sixteen she had been forced to marry General Kern, a man of forty, brutal, coarse, and ignorant. Hurt, she had turned in upon herself, but her disillusioned heart, her unsatisfied senses demanded the love that they did not know. She had lovers, who perverted her physically without reaching her power to love. In spite of her disillusionments she continued to search among men for the one who should at last reveal her to herself. In society almost every door had been closed to her.

She was twenty-eight years old.

The evening was coming to an end in a transparent half-light saturated with the scent of foliage. From time to time a bird, falling asleep, gave a trill that grew slower and slower. It was June, the season of "white nights," when dawn follows twilight after a few uncertain hours. At Trigorskoe the lamps had not been lighted, to avoid attracting mosquitoes.

At first the conversation had dealt with literature, politics, spiritualism; then, as always, it had turned to love. They discussed marriage, platonic love, the rights of passion. Pushkin was in fine fettle. The ladies listened to him, fascinated, like birds before a snake. In the shadow he could see their wide white skirts and the pale halos that were their faces.

Mrs. Kern was listening to him in her favorite pose, her elbow on the arm of her chair, her face resting on the palm of her hand. She felt that he was talking for her, over the other women's heads.

Suddenly he broke off. "Ladies, the evening is almost over. I suggest that we end it at my house. Mrs. Kern has never seen Mikhailovskoe. I should like to show it to her."

"Oh yes!" cried Zizi, delighted not to go to bed. "Oh yes, Mama, order the carriage. We'll take a moonlight drive!"

The ladies rose with a fluttering of skirts, with little nervous laughs, with faces like overexcited cats. Ah, this was unexpected, amusing; this was—how express it?—this was "romantic." Mrs. Ossipov left the room to give the necessary orders. The coachmen were awakened, the neighing horses harnessed.

"Look, look at the moon," Anna murmured, leaning her head against the back of the carriage and gazing upward. The ghostly clarity of the "white night" shed a slight pallor over her face with its sensual lips. Pushkin put his arm around her waist. He felt that everything was permissible in this nocturnal world that seemed almost unreal under the light of the moon.

"The moon is dull," he murmured, smiling.

She made a little face. "Why?"

"I only like the moon when it lights a beautiful countenance."

Annie, devoured by jealousy, kept silent in a corner of her carriage. But what did Annie matter to Pushkin! For the first time in the month that Anna had been at Trigorskoe he was alone with this superb creature. (Annie did not count.)

He had shouted to the coachman to drive fast, to leave the other carriages behind. Finally Mikhailovskoe appeared, flooded with pale white light, framed in black foliage. Pushkin handed out the ladies. The nyanya came running with lamps. The maids brought chairs, opened locked rooms.

"Come, Pushkin, show us around your garden." Netty pouted.

Pushkin gave Mrs. Kern his arm and led her out onto the steps. The other ladies followed, lifting their skirts, as if they were afraid to set foot on the ground. It was fashionable to appear ethereal, delicate, always to need an arm to lean on.

Alexander ran like a schoolboy, leading his companion down long dark walks vaulted over with foliage. She leaned on him heavily, drooping, surrendering herself.

He said, "You remember the first time I saw you, at the Olenins'?"

"Yes, and you were perfectly unbearable."

"It was because I wanted you to pay some attention to me, and you had eyes for no one but that glutton Krilov."

"I was acting Cleopatra. You came up and made my cousin furious by saying, 'This gentleman will doubtless play the asp?'"

"That was jealousy speaking."

"And when you sat down behind me and said in a loud voice, 'Has anyone a right to be so beautiful?'"

"But you really were so beautiful! I remember—you had such a virginal look. Weren't you wearing some sort of cross?"

"Yes—however, all that was very impertinent."

"And you punished me cruelly by leaving without giving me a look."

She smiled. "You looked so unhappy, standing in the entrance and following me with your eyes."

They could no longer hear the ladies' voices. Everyone had probably gone into the house. They were walking alone in the quiet old park, under the tall trees, under the fantastic light of a big moon that looked like a face ravaged by smallpox.

Through the thin soles of her shoes she could feel the great roots that ran across the walks just under the ground. Suddenly she stumbled, almost fell. Pushkin caught her in his arms. For an instant he held her pressed against his body, feeling her warm flesh through his light summer clothing, intoxicated by the sweetish odor of her strong femininity. She freed herself without blushing. He bent and picked something up.

"What are you doing?"

"I'm picking up the stone you stumbled on. I want to keep it."

To go to Riga was a real journey. The only way to travel was by post chaise, in which you had a hard time finding room for your feet between the baskets of provender. You arrived at the relay station worn out, your back as tired as if you had walked the entire distance. And after eating a cold and desiccated meal you shared your bed with an army of fleas.

Mrs. Ossipov was moving about restlessly. Annie was staring into the garden with her eyes full of tears. She was waiting for Pushkin to say good-by to her, and he did not come. Her mother was taking her away by force, out of jealousy, so as not to leave her alone with Alexander—to please him, or at least to break the monotony of his boredom.

Mrs. Kern kept looking impatiently toward the door. She was waiting for Pushkin too. Finally they heard his footsteps and the noise of his iron walking stick. He was on foot and looked distracted. He hardly noticed Annie.

"I have brought you something, a souvenir," he said to Mrs. Kern, handing her a roll of paper. "No, don't read it now," he added almost convulsively as she started to open the roll, and he almost pulled it out of her hands. Anna rose and went to find the casket in which she kept a few letters and a lock of hair from the head of her little daughter, who was at home with her father.

"Alexander Sergeevich," Annie murmured, almost weeping, "I am leaving too."

He nodded distractedly. She took his hands.

"If it depended on me I would not go; I should stay here—to console you!" she said.

Anna returned with the casket. They all went out onto the steps.

"Another departure!" said Pushkin sadly to Anna. "It reminds me of our last meeting in St. Petersburg. Then I saw you get into a carriage and vanish from my life for a long, long time. We seem to be made to meet and then part almost at once."

The wind ruffled his curly hair. He stood there, his head bowed, his arms hanging, forgetting to help Annie into the carriage, unable to hide his grief.

Anna got in. The coachman picked up the reins. She waved her gloved hand, which held a little handkerchief. Before the berlin turned she leaned out and caught a last glimpse of the slender figure buttoned up in an old tight-waisted frock coat with full sleeves.

Then she opened the casket and unrolled Pushkin's present. It was a canto of *Eugene Onegin*, copied without erasures in a fine, slanting hand, and a poem "Dedicated to A. P. Kern":

I remember the divine moment when you appeared before me, like a fleeting vision, like the genius of pure beauty.

For long afterwards, through suffering and sadness, through the noisy vanity of the world, I heard in dreams a tender voice, I saw a lovely face.

Years passed. Storms drove away my dreams of long ago. And I forgot your tender voice and your heavenly face.

My days passed slowly in the shadows and forgetfulness of exile, without God, without tears, without life, without poetry, and without love.

But suddenly my soul reawakened. You appeared before me again, like a fleeting vision, like the genius of pure beauty.

And now my heart beats rapturously once more; once more it knows life, tears, God, poetry, and love.

The Epic

ON SEPTEMBER 1, 1825, THE Emperor Alexander left St. Petersburg for the south of Russia. This latest change of residence was explained as being due to the Empress Elisabeth's state of health. In reality Alexander wanted to escape from his capital. For a long time now Arakcheev, whom he had put at the head of the Council of Ministers charged with dispatching current business during his frequent absences, had ruled in his stead. Alexander contented himself with simply signing the resolutions that his all-powerful favorite sent him. He did not even read them.

His health was not good, and he could feel death approaching. Those about him were frightened by his waxy complexion, by the unhealthy puffiness of a face that had once been so handsome. The Emperor's head was completely bald. Nevertheless he remained elegant and refined in his habits, faithful to frock coats made of the finest English cloths and to a semimilitary cut.

His popularity had lessened greatly. No longer was he the angel or the hero or the man who had taken Paris; he was disliked. The accusation of parricide was more and more openly made.

The prosperity that had come in 1811 and the following years had given way to a long period of economic crisis. The price of bread went steadily downward, particularly after the revolution in Greece, which had seriously disorganized Russian commerce. Capital became scarce, and this state of affairs was aggravated by the conquest of Poland. In 1818, on grounds relating to foreign policy, Alexander had signed with Prussia a customs agreement that had practically opened Russia to German products. The foreign merchandise, against which there was no barrier, poured into Russia, ruining the nascent commerce and industry of the country.

Alexander's foreign policy was unpopular. People said that his early successes had turned his head, that he considered himself the greatest monarch in the world. He was given the ironic title "Emperor of Europe," and accused of neglecting Russia, of hating everything Russian.

He flattered the Poles, who played a pivotal role in his plans. Poland was a wedge thrust into the heart of Prussia. Poland put Berlin within a few days' march from the Russian frontier. . . . While Russia was struggling under the yoke of autocracy Poland had a semblance of a constitution, a semblance of liberty, a semblance of law.

All this dissatisfied the Russians. The reactionaries demanded a pure and simple annexation of Poland—let a governor be sent there, as to the other provinces. Others demanded that Russia should at least be given what Poland had: a constitution.

The army—the army that he had wanted to build up as a sort of appanage of the crown, an instrument of his power, cost heavily and was not reliable. The memory of the French campaign was not yet obliterated, after ten years.

The soldiers had breathed the air of liberty and had got it into their heads that they were there to serve the country, not the Emperor.

They did not so easily accept life in barracks, which ran for a term of twenty years, the mechanical discipline, the perpetual standing at attention, the parades, the reviews, the incessant orders beloved by their chiefs, the Emperor and the grand dukes, who believed themselves to be soldiers body and soul because they liked nice shiny buttons.

Napoleon, whose shadow still hung over Europe, enjoyed an extraordinary and unexpected prestige in the Russian Army. On the other hand, Louise XVIII, who had been brought back to Paris in the Russian baggage train, was not popular. The soldiers called him "Dixhuitov."

Many of the young officers belonged to the "secret society." Alexander knew that he was threatened with assassination. Sometimes he thought of his father, stifled under a pillow while he mounted guard.

He could not even die quietly. He had no heir. His brother Constantine was to succeed him. But he knew that the Grand Duke—who was at Warsaw in supreme command of the Polish Army—had an insurmountable repugnance for the crown.

The night of March 11, 1801, on which his father had been assassinated with his brother's knowledge, had fixed an indelible terror in his soul.

Besides, Constantine had been divorced and was morganatically married to a Polish lady who was not even descended from one of the great families of the kingdom. The Grand Duke Nicholas, on the other hand, had a son already, and his wife—a gaunt Prussian princess—was own daughter to Queen Louise.

Constantine's abdication in favor of his younger brother —younger by seventeen years—had been secretly decided upon by the imperial family. But how would the country take the change? For twenty-five years prayers had been offered in the churches for the health of the Czarevitch Constantine. . . . He was living in "free" Poland—yet another reason for thinking that he was different from other princes. Nicholas, on the other hand, was not popular at all.

On November 25 the Empress Dowager and the authorities in St. Petersburg received a message from Taganrog informing them that the Emperor was seriously ill. The question of the succession immediately became acute. Orders were sent to the provinces to keep fresh horses on hand for the courier who should bring the news of the Emperor's death.

On the twenty-sixth the court breathed again. The day's news, which dated from November 18, was better. His Majesty's condition left room for hope.

Alexander died on November 19, at 10:50 A.M. He had escaped the traditional death of a Russian Czar—assassination by a member of his family.

Confusion reigned in the palace. At all costs an interregnum must be avoided. The throne must not remain vacant a single day. The French formula was the only acceptable one: "The King is dead, long live the King!"

Constantine did not want the throne and the army did not want Nicholas. Count Miloradovich, governor general of St. Petersburg, who was constantly at the palace, began to threaten: "The army is waiting to swear allegiance to the Emperor Constantine. If Grand Duke Nicholas assumes power I cannot be responsible for my men." Outside the palace he admitted: "When a man has sixty thousand bayonets in his pocket, he can speak up and stick to it." He did not fail to avail himself of the privilege.

Nicholas was intimidated. He hastened to swear allegiance to his brother. A line formed in the chapel to swear fidelity to the new Emperor on the Bible. In the haste and confusion the army swore allegiance before the ministers.

Constantine I's reign had begun. Coins were minted with his effigy, hundreds of thousands of copies of his portrait were hastily reproduced.

As for the Emperor himself, he was nowhere to be found. He was thought to be at Taganrog, or on his way to the capital. In reality he had not budged from Warsaw. He was happy there, with his dogs, his mistresses, his children, and his soldiers, and he flew into a rage when anyone addressed him as "Your Majesty."

Couriers galloping posthaste between Warsaw and St. Petersburg passed one another, carrying supplicating messages from the Empress Dowager and rude messages from Constantine. He asked but one thing: to be left in peace, God damn it! Go to St. Petersburg? He was not even thinking of it. Let Their Majesties find the best way out they could. He washed his hands of the matter.

Meanwhile the country was waiting to know who was to be its new master. No one believed in the official version of events, in which the two grand dukes were supposed to be tossing the crown back and forth like a ball. Yet the official version was the true one. There were rumors that Constantine was in flight, in prison, assassinated. . . . Public opinion was accustomed to these palace revolutions, after which the corpses were thrown into the Neva.

On December 12, almost a month after the Emperor

Alexander's death, Constantine's final answer arrived: he refused the throne. The ceremony of swearing allegiance to the Emperor Nicholas I was set for Monday, December 14.

The curtain raiser was over. The tragedy began.

The opposition was everywhere and nowhere. Everyone was discontented: the serfs, the soldiers who spent twenty-five years out of their lives in barracks, the merchants who were suffering from the economic crisis, the nobles who sold their bread at a loss, the manufacturers who could not find capital. But this general discontent, which could have given birth to the revolution, gave birth to nothing but bad feeling. The opposition was not organized. It had no leader. It had no aim. The "secret society," which had taken its very name, Union of Virtue, from the German organization called the *Tugendbund,* was weak, disorganized, divided. Its two divisions, the Northern Section and the Southern Section; each had its own leaders, its own ideas, its own general staff and plan of action. The Southern Section were Jacobins who wanted a democratic, equalitarian republic. The Northern Section asked no more than the abolition of serfdom and a constitutional monarchy. To this timorous and feeble Northern Section fell the task of directing the revolution.

The conspirators realized that the moment was propitious: the throne had been vacant for three weeks. Nicholas, already unpopular on account of his reactionary ideas, was in a disadvantageous position and appeared to be a usurper. It would be enough to intensify the rumors that were already in circulation: that Constantine had been assassinated, that he had intended to abolish serfdom and shorten military service. To raise the army would be all the easier because of the fact that it had already sworn allegiance to Constantine and that to swear faith to Nicholas now seemed a sort of sacrilege.

But they were only a handful of young officers, graduates of the imperial lyceum of Tsarskoe Selo—not one of whom could answer for an entire regiment. The best of them were dreamers, the worst, arrant braggarts.

But their principal weakness was that they were revolutionaries who were afraid of the revolution. Their motto was that of the enlightened despots: For the people, but without the people. They were a little suspicious of the people.

At dawn on December 14 seven hundred soldiers of the Moscow Regiment, flags flying, left their barracks, led by two officers who were in the conspiracy, and marched to Senate Square. There they were to join the other revolting regiments, prevent the Senate from swearing allegiance, march on the Winter Palace, force Nicholas to abdicate, and secure a liberal constitution and the abolition of serfdom.

They found the square empty: no police, no soldiers; no enemies, no allies. The windows of the Senate were dark, the senators having sworn allegiance during the night. The first point on the program had failed.

The officers drew up their men facing the four buildings that surrounded the square and waited in the cold. The wind whipped their flag. Their feet were frozen. The public buildings seemed to stare at the men through rows of empty windows. And still nothing happened.

From time to time the officers ordered the men to shout, "Down with Nicholas!" "Long live Constantine, long live the constitution!" The wretched, ill-nourished, ill-treated soldiers shouted. They knew no more of Nicholas than they did of Constantine. The strange word "constitution" meant nothing to them. Some of them thought that it was the name of Constantine's wife.

The square began to fill with people who were sympathetic to the insurgents and shouted words of encouragement. The leaders of the conspiracy arrived and, seeing the insufficient number of soldiers, went to find reinforcements. Some of them never returned. It was not cowardice but discouragement. All seemed lost before anything had even begun.

Some hours later another detachment of infantry joined the insurgents. Then the marines arrived, won over by two officers.

Meanwhile, Nicholas had decided to concentrate the forces that had remained loyal to him. He felt that he was entering unknown ground. How many soldiers had he? How many did the insurgents have? Everything was confused, uncertain, unstable.

At noon a group of veiled women had left the Winter Palace in a hired carriage. They were the two empresses, with the young Czarevitch and the princesses. The two czarinas—the younger and the elder—conversed in German. They were both Prussian.

Back at Senate Square, the insurgents were completely surrounded. Both sides were waiting for orders that did not come. Both sides were wondering whether to fire on "their fellows." The Czar's soldiers felt no hatred for the insurgents, who wore the same uniform as themselves. They felt more enmity toward the crowd, which was throwing bricks and paving stones and sticks at them. Besides, they did not want Nicholas either.

It was now three o'clock, and the short northern day was ending. With twilight there came a mauve fog, which chilled the soldiers in their thin cloaks and tight boots. None of them had gloves; none of them had eaten anything since daybreak. They fired into the air to relieve their boredom.

The insurgents were expecting the loyal troops to come over to their side, Nicholas was expecting the insurgents to surrender. Finally he sensed that to remain inactive was growing dangerous. The crowd showed its sympathy with the insurgents more and more clearly. The workmen who were building the St. James Cathedral threw bricks and pieces of wood at the loyal troops. At the first shots the crowd around the Czar began to put on their hats, as if in defiance. He shouted, "Hats off!" and then muttered in French to General Toll, "A fine beginning for a reign!"

The square was now surrounded by troops who had just sworn allegiance to him but he still hesitated. It would not do to order a cavalry charge—the horses were slipping on the ice. There was nothing for it but grapeshot.

He was urged to have it over with. He shouted, "Fire!" but no report came. An officer leaped to the ground, ran to the cannoneer, and asked him why he did not fire. "They are our brothers, Your Excellency," the soldier answered, weeping. The officer struck him in the face, lit the fuse, and fired. But he had aimed too high. The grapeshot rattled into the second-story windows of the Senate House.

The second shot was better aimed. The insurgents broke ranks and fled; it was every man for himself. They had not been prepared for grapeshot. They ran in all directions.

The majority, overflowing the deep ranks massed along the quays, tried to cross the frozen Neva. Balls fell whistling, breaking the ice around them. Many of them were drowned.

In Senate Square the work of removing the dead and wounded began. A hundred corpses were laid in a long line in the great nave of the new church, construction on which had reached the second story. Among them was the headless body of a twelve-year-old boy, the drummer boy of the Moscow Regiment. Such was the effect of grapeshot at short range.

The first Russian revolution had aborted.

The night was transparent and unquiet, as if Nature herself knew that a crime was about to be committed. It seemed that the sun had only just set, yet the sky was already green. The city was full of strange noises, sounds half stifled in the silence. The river sent little plashing waves to lick the granite stones of the quays. Cocks crowed in nearby villages. Here and there a drum rolled, followed by its echoes. It was four o'clock in the morning.

A detachment of grenadiers entered the parade ground of the Peter and Paul Fortress, St. Petersburg's famous bastille. The soldiers marched in goose step, after the Prussian fashion, with the mechanical precision of automatons.

At the far end of the parade ground, directly on the bank of the Neva and facing the Church of the Trinity, a strange apparatus, somewhat like a pair of scales, had been erected: the gibbet. Beneath it was a trench, concealed by the planking.

On reaching the gibbet the soldiers moved aside, exposing to view the five men they had surrounded. They were

the "Decembrists," Ryleev, Muravev, Kakhovski, Bestu-
zhev, and Pestel. They were dressed in white shirts trimmed
with black bands on which was the inscription, "State
Criminals." They walked laboredly, with a noise of irons
and chains.

Several days beforehand at two o'clock in the morning
the ceremony of stripping them of their rank had taken
place. Clad in their scarlet uniforms (most of them were
officers in the guards), they were led into the court of the
fortress, where their respective regiments were drawn up.
Each was made to kneel before his own men. In this position their decorations, their epaulets, and their gold braid
were torn off. Then their swords—which had been filed
beforehand—were broken over their heads. The filing had
been badly done and they were half killed in the course of
the ceremony.

The five executioners muffled the condemned men in
sacks that hung down to their waists, then they led the
stumbling prisoners under the gibbet. Each made sure
that the knot was well greased before he put the noose
around his victim's neck. Then they stepped back. Moved
by machinery, the planks that hid the trench from view
began to draw apart, screeching.

The victims, shaken by horrible convulsions, now hung
suspended over the void. Suddenly an inhuman shriek
pierced the silence. The ropes that had been used were
strong enough to bear the weight of a man, but the weight
of the chains and irons had been forgotten and three of the
ropes broke. Three men fell heavily into the trench, wound-
ing themselves on the planks, which had not yet been
completely withdrawn. The priest who had come to minister to the condemned men dropped in a faint.

The executioners went down into the trench and removed the sacks from the hanged men. They were still alive, bruised and bleeding from the fall, their necks half broken. "All my life I never succeeded in anything," said Ryleev with trembling lips, "not even in dying!"

Voices rose from the crowd: "A man can't be executed twice!" Someone shouted: "Poor Russia—where they don't even know how to hang a man properly!"

The officer sent for ropes, but the shops were still closed, so there was nothing to do but wait. The condemned men were made to sit on the ground. The military band played lively marches to occupy the crowd. Half an hour later the ropes arrived and the executioners finished hanging the condemned men. This time all went well. The soldiers reformed in column and marched off, with the band in front giving the cadence in the Prussian fashion. The spectators began to drift away.

The sun, which had long since risen in a deep, blue, cloudless sky, dusted its blond light over the yellow, trampled grass, the heaps of refuse, and the gibbet, which no longer resembled a pair of scales because now it bore fruit —five bodies through which imperceptible shivers still ran.

The same morning a very dark girl, dressed in white, appeared on the walk that led to the lake of Tsarskoe Selo. It was Miss Rossetti, one of the Czarina's young maids of honor.

At eight o'clock the day promised to be warm and still; the sun was already high. In the distance the hideous architecture of the palace of Tsarskoe Selo—built in the style of Potsdam and painted yellow—was visible through the leaves. In the park everything was still and green. The bright, unrippled surface of the lake reflected the enormous oaks that had been planted in the days of Catherine II.

Suddenly the girl stopped short. Across the lake she had seen the Emperor, dressed in his general's uniform. She hesitated a moment. The Czar liked pretty women. He advertised his affection for his family, and every afternoon at five o'clock tea enacted a perfect little scene of domestic happiness. But the Empress was thin, and besides, he liked a change. She did not protest, and she received his mistresses.

The younger and prettier maids of honor feared meeting the Czar alone in the corridors of the palace. Miss Rossetti was one of his favorites. Nicholas called her by her first name and entered her apartments without knocking, even if she happened to be washing her feet.

But he had not seen her and went on playing with his dog, a big Irish setter with intelligent eyes. He threw his handkerchief into the lake, waited until the current had carried it out to the middle, then loosed the dog, who plunged delightedly into the cold water. The Czar looked pale and sad. His gestures were made with the intense application of a man who is trying to free his mind of an obsessing idea.

Suddenly the girl saw a footman running toward the Emperor. He said something to the Czar, who turned and cried (the wind carried his words to the girl's ears): "A courier from St. Petersburg?" And he hurried to the palace.

The dog came out of the water, shaking himself. Seeing no one where he had left his master a few moments before, he dropped the delicate handkerchief marked with an *N* surmounted by an eagle, and trotted toward the palace, leaving a wet trail behind him.

On July 13, 1826, the Court Circular announced that the Emperor, after praying for a long time in the chapel, had shut himself up in his study and had spent the greater part of the day there.

At five o'clock His Majesty appeared at the Czarina's tea. He looked unwell and spoke but little.

ii

Pushkin felt unhappy, troubled, nervous. He could not work. At night he often waked and lay thinking of his dead comrades. When the rhymes would not come he drew mechanically on the margins of his paper—not heads and women's feet, but a gibbet bearing five hanged men. That picture shaped itself under his pen over and over, like a familiar spirit, like a sickly obsession. He, too, perhaps . . .

The dead were dead, but imprisonment for one hundred and twenty-one comrades was terrible. Almost all of his friends were in the plot. Several of his school chums had been arrested in Senate Square, at the head of the revolting troops. He had known every one of the hanged men personally.

Around him now there was a great emptiness. Pushchin was in Siberia, Trubetskoi in Siberia, Volkonski—Maria Raevski's husband—in Siberia. Alexander Raevski was imprisoned in a fortress, Küchelbecker was about to be deported.

He himself was seriously compromised. Exile had saved him from actual participation in the conspiracy. But without knowing it he had been the bard of the Decembrists: his poems were read at their meetings to arouse enthusiasm. His name had been mentioned several times in the course of the trial.

Under these circumstances anything was preferable to his enforced immobility. He lived in the expectation of trouble—which was worse than trouble itself. He had destroyed his journal, several hundred letters, a quantity of verse. Of *The Prophet*—a poem as hard as a diamond, of truly biblical grandeur—there remained only a fragment, but what a fragment!

> *Athirst in spirit, through the gloom*
> *Of an unpeopled waste I blundered,*
> *And saw a six-winged seraph loom*
> *Where the two pathways met and sundered.*
> *He laid his fingers on my eyes:*
> *His touch lay soft as slumber lies,—*
> *And like an eagle's, his crag shaken,*
> *Did my prophetic eyes awaken.*
> *Upon my ears his fingers fell*
> *And sound rose—stormy swell on swell:*
> *I heard the spheres revolving, chiming,*
> *The angels in their soaring sweep,*
> *The monsters moving in the deep,*
> *The green vine in the valley climbing.*
> *And from my mouth the seraph wrung*
> *Forth by its roots my sinful tongue;*
> *The evil things and vain it babbled*
> *His hand drew forth and so effaced,*
> *And the wise serpent's tongue he placed*
> *Between my lips with hand blood-dabbled;*

And with a sword he clove my breast,
Plucked out the heart he made beat higher,
And in my stricken bosom pressed
Instead a coal of living fire.
Upon the wastes, a lifeless clod,
I lay, and heard the voice of God:
"Arise, oh, prophet, watch and hearken,
And with my Will thy soul engird,
Roam the gray seas, the roads that darken,
And burn men's hearts with this, my Word."[1]

But what the Prophet saw was known only to the flames
that danced on the hearth at Mikhailovskoe.

[1] From *The Poems, Prose and Plays of Alexander Pushkin,* Copyright,
1936, by Random House, Inc.

The Comedy

PUSHKIN

THE EMPEROR WAS IN GOOD humor. A few days earlier he had been crowned in the ancient fortress of the czars, the white-walled gilt-roofed Kremlin. Everything had gone well, without the slightest mishap, without any of the catastrophes that usually mark such occasions.

The coronation festivities were still going on. Moscow boomed like a drum under the gilded dust of a dry, sunny autumn. The population of the city had almost doubled, until the poorest rooms were worth their weight in gold. Whinnying horses, shouting coachmen, wheels rattling over ill-paved streets, filled the air of the ancient capital with a perpetual roar. It had been a long time since anyone had seen such a splendid and thronged coronation. The Emperor himself had wished it so. His gift to the country on his accession had been to hang five men and send a hundred and twenty-five more to Siberia. That memory must be effaced. The pool of blood in which his reign had begun must be washed out.

The morning after the uprising he had given orders that the bodies must be disposed of within three days, so the prefect of police had simply thrown them into the Neva at various points where there were holes in the ice. The city was full of disquieting rumors. People said that the police, in their haste, had thrown the wounded into the river with the dead, that at some points the crust over the river was lined with corpses frozen into the ice.

Orders were given to stop these rumors. Nicholas had become Emperor but he had remained a general. He was not a half convert to liberal ideas, as Alexander had been. When he gave an order it admitted of no discussion. He had not been a pupil of the republican Laharpe nor had he read Locke and Rousseau. Indeed, he was not interested in intellectual matters; he read very little.

In his whole person there was something heavy, unmoving, and cold that inspired boredom and fear. His ideas were like himself: they were solemn and immovable. His soul was square, like his shoulders. He often raised his eyes to heaven, as if to call the Lord to witness. He was an excellent actor.

He had returned from Senate Square transfigured. It was there, amid the whistling grapeshot, that he had been crowned Emperor. It was there that he had realized his mission: to re-establish order, to crush subversion, to checkmate revolt. Alexander had slackened the reins too much. Conspiracies were in fashion. His reign, like Louis XIV's, had begun with a Fronde. But already things were different. No longer was the government criticized at every turn, as it had been previously. The country was already feeling the new Emperor's strong hand.

Yes, his "friends of the fourteenth," his friends the Decembrists, had given him a good lesson, a lesson that would last him a lifetime. But the Czar of Russia could not be made to tremble with impunity.

The fact is that he had trembled. Like many nervous
men, he had never been brave. A thunderstorm, a shot,
made him turn pale. He was afraid to have a tooth pulled.
It had cost him something to expose himself to the gunfire,
to enter the crowd of rioters. To those around him he had
said, with a sort of controlled despair, "Keep your distance
—they are going to fire at me."

But he had taken his revenge for all the disagreeable
moments they had put him through. He had seen them—
the Jacobins, the would-be Septembrists—defeated, pitiful,
repentant. Where his officials had failed he had succeeded.
He had wrung a complete confession from them—every
name, every detail.

He had discovered that he had the soul of a prosecuting
attorney. To be Czar was a fine thing; to be a policeman
was intoxicating. He had played the whole gamut of feelings before the accused—outraged majesty, indignation,
pity, wrath. Dressed in his green general's uniform, with
the sash that ran diagonally from shoulder to waist, he had
received them one at a time, imposing and majestic, terrible
as an offended divinity. Then he became human: he was
their general, they were his officers; he reproached them
with their treachery, begged them to confess everything,
in the name of Russia, of their wives, of their families. . . .

He walked rapidly up and down, taking long strides,
like a wild beast in a cage, then drew near and fixed the
trembling prisoner with his heavy gray eyes, the eyes that
he had inherited from his insane father and which sometimes made women faint.

Half in French, half in Russian, he overwhelmed the
palpitating prisoners: "Prince Trubetskoi, colonel in the

guards—what a name! What a family! You have ruined your family, Colonel!"

To another: "What do you mean by your filthy word of honor! You have no idea of honor!"

"I regret seeing an old comrade in this situation. You must see that you were deceived, that you deceived others. Come, don't aggravate your error. Confess everything!"

And they confessed everything, they accused themselves, they named everyone, overwhelmed by the very immensity of their defeat. They were caught in the trap, ready to think that he would be generous—so ready that, until the very last day, they did not believe that their sentence would be executed.

When they had nothing more to tell him that he did not already know he sent them to the commander of the Peter and Paul Fortress with detailed instructions as to the treatment they were to receive: "Put him in irons; treat him severely." "Treat him better than the others; give him tea." "Treat him very severely, but give him writing materials if he asks for them." Signed, "Nicholas, Emperor and King."

Like his illustrious ancestor Peter, he did not disdain to put his hand to the wheel. He had not gone so far as to hang them himself, but he had nearly done so. It was he who had worked out the procedure for the executions, in minute detail, down to the hour at which it was to be over —four o'clock precisely.

Now all that was far away. The five leaders had been hanged, the rest were in Siberia, which was not much better. He was seated solidly on the throne that the Decembrist storm had shaken so rudely. The order that he loved so much was at last re-established.

But he needed a merciful gesture. Oh, he did not want it

to cost much. What he needed was something harmless, something that would not imperil the work he had done. A gesture but not an act.

And then he remembered the poet whose verses had been found among the Decembrists' papers. He had been in exile six years—consequently no direct participation in the plot. At once guilty and not guilty. . . . To recall Pushkin would have many advantages; it would rally the women and the intellectuals to the regime. Besides, there was no harm in having a great poet on hand. Had not Louis XIV had Molière, Boileau, and Racine? He could be kept busy doing something useful—writing a chronicle, a memoir, in short something less frivolous than poetry.

When his intention became known a court lady said, "I have decided to make it up with the Czar—he is recalling Pushkin." Her remark was immediately reported to him.

Whereupon he wrote to the governor of Pskov, ordering Pushkin, Esquire, to be brought to Moscow. Meticulous as always, he added a postscript: "This person will travel under the guard of a courier but will not be treated as a prisoner." And he sent a laconic note to his chief of staff: "Bring Pushkin to my apartments as soon as he arrives."

ii

Nicholas stood near the monumental chimney of his study. The fire lighted his smooth face from below and made the white scarf stand out against his bottle-green uniform. As always, there was something dead in the look of his heavy gray eyes. He stood stiffly, as he would be painted in an official portrait.

The usher entered and announced:

"The author Pushkin."

He was accustomed to announcing generals, princes, colonels, governors. In his mouth the strange word "author" took on a slightly derogatory sound.

"Admit him," said the Emperor shortly.

Someone entered. Nicholas, who had intentionally looked away, turned his eyes upon the newcomer slowly. His face was so still that one would not have thought it alive. Silence fell heavily.

The Emperor's eyes passed over the thin face, wan with fatigue; the long, curly side whiskers; the traveling cape, rumpled and gray with dust. He was satisfied by what he saw. His orders had been carried out to the letter. Pushkin was to face his Emperor exhausted, dirty, used up, stiff from travel, so that he should feel more intensely the extent of the mercy he was to receive.

Pushkin had just accomplished in three days a journey that ordinarily took six. He had asked to be allowed to shave, to brush his wrinkled clothes, to stretch his limbs. The answer had been, "Afterward."

It was the third Romanov he had met. The first had knocked his cap off with his crop. The second had persecuted him for six years and sent him into exile for a few words in a letter. What would the third do?

Finally the Czar broke the silence.

"Good morning, Pushkin. I suppose thou art more than glad to have been recalled?"

Pushkin instinctively raised his eyebrows. It was the first

time he had seen the Czar; the familiarity of his address was unexpected.

He bowed respectfully. Nicholas motioned him to approach.

"My brother had exiled you, not without cause. I pardon you and restore you to liberty. I hope that this time you will know how to make better use of it." He felt the necessity for a greater show of amiability. Without any transition he took the poet's arm and proceeded to walk up and down the room with him. "Between ourselves," he said almost confidentially, "you have committed follies enough. Youth must have its fling—I know that. But I hope that from henceforth you will be sensible and that nothing will come between us."

"That would make me very happy, sire," said Pushkin. The Czar held out his large, cold, white hand. Into it Pushkin put his, which was small and hot.

A question had been burning Nicholas's lips ever since the beginning of the interview. He finally decided to ask it:

"Tell me, what would you have done if you had been in St. Petersburg on the fourteenth of December?"

"All my friends were in the plot, sire. I could have done nothing but join my comrades. Only my absence saved me." He felt that he must make a concession and added: "I am very glad of it now."

The Czar smiled. He felt both satisfied and irritated: satisfied by Pushkin's sincerity, and irritated because in his heart of hearts he had hoped for a different answer. He could not understand the fact that so many people had risen against his legitimate authority. He put his hand in his waistcoat—a gesture that made him look like Napoleon.

"What are you writing now?"

"Nothing, sire. The censorship is too severe."

"Why do you write things that the censors will not pass?"

"The censors let nothing pass."

"Very well, if the censorship troubles you, I will be your only censor. Anything that you write you shall bring first to me, and I myself will give the authorization to print it."

For the first time Pushkin's tired face lighted up.

"Thank you, sire," he cried. "That is truly royal!"

Nicholas's face darkened imperceptibly. This rhymester dared to judge what was royal and what was not? His heavy eyes swung back to Pushkin, who—impertinence or ignorance of the etiquette?—was warming his icy feet with his back to the fireplace. Almost voluptuously the thought came to Nicholas that he had only to make a gesture and Pushkin would go to join his comrades in Siberia. But he restrained himself. Like his brother, he could dissimulate.

"Well, let us go and announce the good news," he said, taking the poet's arm. They left the room together—Pushkin thin and short, the Czar tall, square, theatrical.

"Gentlemen," said the Czar, stopping on the threshold and casting a circular glance over the crowd of uniformed courtiers that filled the antechamber. "Gentlemen," he repeated. "Here is the new Pushkin. *My* Pushkin."

An hour later, bathed, perfumed, the marks of travel removed from his clothes, Alexander was dining at his uncle's.

Vasili Lvovich was exultant. "Just taste this wine, Alexander—go on, taste it! Pure nectar, pure ambrosia, on my honor. It is straight from Bordeaux."

Sergei Sobolveski was announced. He entered, wearing

butter-yellow gloves and a flowered waistcoat that had come from the Rue St. Honoré.

"Permit me to congratulate you, my dear fellow," he said. "I have only just heard of your return, and here I am! I was at Marshal de Marmont's ball—the French ambassador. Suddenly I heard the Emperor say to Bludov: 'I have just been talking to the most intelligent man in Russia. Can you guess who? Pushkin!' Come here and let me embrace you, to convince myself that it is really true."

"Are you glad that I am back?"

"What a question!"

"Will you do something for me?"

"Anything."

"Go to Count Tolstoi's and tell him that I demand satisfaction immediately. His conditions shall be mine."

"But satisfaction for what?" stammered Sobolevski, flabbergasted.

"For having given currency to infamous rumors concerning me."

"I don't understand you. Explain yourself."

Pushkin mentioned the rumors that had been circulating about him before his exile. He was supposed to have been given a whipping in the secret dungeons of the police. For six years he had waited for this moment; for six years, through all the vicissitudes of exile, he had cherished—with what somber ardor!—the thought of vengeance.

"But see here, Alexander, all that was six years ago. You aren't going to risk your life for that!" cried Sobolevski.

"A promise is a promise," Pushkin answered quietly. "Gentlemen, your health," and he raised to his lips a glass full of amber-colored wine.

iii

Princess Volkonski's white-and-gold salon—a little Russian Versailles where the nation's celebrities received their final consecration of fame—was one pole of Moscow's artistic and fashionable life. The princess's guests sang and acted plays and tasted what the princess affectedly called "the pleasures of the mind."

Like every other celebrity, Alexander was expected to appear in this fashionable temple of art once or twice a month, to drop a few witticisms by way of food for St. Petersburg's empty minds, and to vanish before the first candles had burned out.

All this no longer amused him. On his return from Mikhailovskoe it had pleased him, when he went to the theater, to see every opera glass focused on his seat in the orchestra. He had become drunk with his fame as with strong wine. But that kind of drunkenness had its mornings after, too.

At first Princess Volkonski's subtle flatteries, all the delicate incense that surrounded him, had pleased him. Now he was tired of it, as he was of everything. For Princess Volkonski, as for all the other hostesses who contended for the favor of his presence, he was nothing but a number on the program.

The princess was just coming to meet him, glittering, her bare shoulders emerging from a tight bodice, her skirt billowing over taffeta underskirts.

"Ah, Alexander, at last! We are to have the joy of hearing you. What new products of your genius have you brought us?" she simpered in French. She took his arm. "There is something that I must tell you. The other day the Emperor asked Miss Rossetti, 'Why doesn't Pushkin enter the service?' and she answered, 'But, sire, he is serving already *dans le génie*.'[1] What do you think of that?" She touched his arm with her fan. "And now excuse me; I must go and see if the buffet is ready."

Zinaida Volkonski had too much of everything: too much wealth, too much beauty, too much wit. Her blue eyes were too big, her figure too luxuriant, her paintings too authentic, and even her voice too big for a simple amateur stage. She made you want to say, "Don't put in any more!"

Alexander stopped a passing footman, took a glass of champagne, and leaned against a doorframe. For a long time he had loved all these lights, the confused noise of conversation mixed with the strains of an orchestra, the wild stamping of the mazurkas, the gossip, the confidences whispered behind a pearl fan, the women with their bare, powdered shoulders—all the atmosphere of a ball, the lack of which he had felt so passionately during his exile. Now he was tired of it. He felt bored as he watched the women pass with swirling skirts, laughing, whispering—and most of them had husbands or brothers or friends who had been hanged or exiled or imprisoned.

After their defeat the Decembrists had been betrayed and renounced by their families. It was a scramble to see who could be most cowardly, most abject. The day on which the Decembrist Volkonski, Zinaida's brother, had set off, shaved like a convict, in the custody of two guards, to travel

[1] An untranslatable play on words. *Dans le génie* may mean either "in the engineering corps" or "as a genius."

to his Siberian prison, his mother, the old Princess Volkonski, had opened the ball with the Emperor at the Imperial Theater.

This utter rout, this moral devil-take-the-hindmost, had profoundly disgusted Pushkin. He thought of it while the couples passed before him in a cloud of skirts. Zinaida was whirling round and round. Was she thinking, while she waltzed, of her brother who was rotting—a living corpse—in a Siberian mine?

Suddenly noticing a woman who had just entered, he turned pale. She was standing in the doorway looking around, screwing up her shortsighted eyes a little. Maria . . . Maria Raevski—or rather, Maria Volkonski, Zinaida's sister-in-law, the prisoner's wife, the one woman whose behavior made up for all the betrayals, all the disavowals.

The princess went to receive her and greeted her with a kiss. Two more different women could not be imagined: Zinaida blond, covered with diamonds, dripping with perfume, her bare shoulders looking as if they sprang directly from her full pink skirt; Maria simple, pale with weariness, her clear eyes underlined by blue shadows, a braid the color of night wound round her small, aristocratic head with its irregular features.

At her appearance a murmur of curiosity and admiration ran through the room. The women whispered behind their fans, bending their heads; the men fell back as she advanced.

This frail young woman—less than two years a wife and mother—was following a husband twenty years older than herself into the frozen Siberian steppes.

Alexander could not keep his eyes off Maria. How well he understood now the prophetic words whispered at the hour of parting before a violet sea: "But for myself, I dream of a different destiny." Her action, he knew, was a gesture of pure devotion. The whole story, heard bit by bit in the salons, came back to him now, and he pictured it to himself —the young, new mother, buried in the country, struggling against the opposition of her family in order to follow her old husband to prison! "You gave me Sergei as a husband. My duty is to be with him."

Now she was sitting by herself, between two marble columns, in a little salon adjoining the ballroom, from which the sound of a harpsichord and the baritone of Zinaida's official singer, Count Ricci, could be heard.

He finally found courage to approach, took her limp hand, and touched it with his lips.

"Oh, it's you, Alexander?" she said unaffectedly, as if they had parted only the evening before. "Heavens, what a man you've grown up to be!"

"And you—you are still the same, Maria, only even more beautiful and—how can I put it?—quite glorified," he said, referring to the attention she was arousing. He bent and murmured: "I understand now why those gentlemen would not allow me to join their 'secret society'; I was unworthy of the honor. Yes, I mean it," he cried as she shook her head.

Zinaida approached, rustling, holding her skirt between two fingers. Maria seized her hand.

"Ask them to sing again! Music . . . perhaps I shall never hear it again!"

Tears rose to her great black eyes. She hid her face in the palm of her hand. Zinaida left them, pressing a handkerchief to her lips. Pushkin seized her small brown hand.

"Maria, listen to me. . . . I intend to write a book on Pugachev. I must go to the sites, I'll cross the Urals, and

I'll come and ask you to give me shelter, in the Nerchinsk Mines—may I?"

A man's voice had begun to sing in the small salon. She listened, transfigured, forgetting to hide the tears that flowed, fast and warm, down her thin cheeks.

The Romance

BEFORE ENTERING THE BALL-
room Alexander stopped in front of a mirror, smoothed his
hair, and adjusted the ruffles of his shirt. A ruffled front
set off his figure to advantage. He wore an extremely tight-
waisted coat and close-fitting white trousers with straps,
which outlined the still fine curve of his calves. His clothes
came from a good tailor, but he had aged and he looked
tired.

Tired he was: tired of balls, of the sleepless nights during
which he gambled away whole volumes he had not yet
written, tired of being spied on by the police, vilified by
journalists, flattered by hostesses, and betrayed by his mistresses. He had thought he was a prisoner at Mikhailovskoe,
but here was the real prison.

Boris Godunov, the first Russian play worthy of the international stage, lay buried in his drawer, beyond hope of
being published. The illustrious censor to whom it had
been presented in person had written on the margin of the
manuscript: "I consider that the author's object would be
achieved if he were to transform his comedy, with the
necessary purification, into a historical sketch or a novel in

the style of Walter Scott." It was thus that the Czar exercised his right to censor Pushkin's works. Besides, Nicholas had not even read the "comedy." The comment that indicated such a refined literary taste emanated from General Benkendorf, chief of police, who had the Emperor's absolute confidence.

And so, freed from the official censorship, which—unintelligent though it was—yet had some connection with literature, he had fallen under the direct supervision of the police. The police . . . they never let go their hold. He could not leave St. Petersburg for twenty-four hours without receiving a sharp letter from Benkendorf, scolding him as if he were a schoolboy. For he was fixed to his place of residence like a serf or a Jew. There were times when he thought the new Czar's mercy was heavier than the old Czar's persecutions.

Finally he made up his mind to enter the ballroom. Footmen were passing among the dancers, going to snuff the candles, which were nearly burned down and shedding hot, greasy tears. The music could be heard sporadically above the clatter of the mazurka, the noise of conversation, and the sound of glasses. When the women turned in a waltz they showed their ankles, crossed by the black ribbons of their slippers.

The constraint resulting from the Emperor's presence had long since given place to the atmosphere of a ball, composed of perfumes, perspiration, dust, and scandal. The Czar himself had set the example by offering his gloved hand to one of the prettiest women in Moscow. The Czarina was dancing with a fat notable, who pulled in his stomach in order to avoid touching the Empress with that prosaic part of his anatomy.

"You're not dancing, Môssieu Pushkin?"

Alexander turned. Princess Trubetskoi stood before him, holding her fan so as to half cover her naked and powdered old shoulders.

"No, excuse me, madame," he said shortly. The old woman's eyes followed his own as they returned to a slight feminine figure standing motionless at the Emperor's right. It was a very young girl, almost a child. Her white dress, not cut very low, revealed a long delicate neck and the pure, slight shoulders of an adolescent. Her corsage outlined a budding breast, a slender waist—the rest was lost in a vaporous skirt that looked like the corolla of a rose turned upside down. The girl's white forehead was encircled by a gold *ferronnière* whose warm color brought out the transparence of her faultless complexion and the luster of her black hair, which she wore à la Anne of Austria, with charming corkscrew curls down her temples and cheeks. Everything in this beautiful madonnalike face was of a superhuman perfection.

"You are looking at our Natalya?" the princess murmured into Pushkin's ear. "She is certainly worthy of a poet's homage. A trifle thin—but that will pass," she added in the tone of a woman who had once been beautiful herself. "I really must introduce you: you were made to know each other. You are our first romantic poet, and she is our one perfect romantic beauty!"

He did not reply to her ingenious compliment. He could not wait to be beside the girl.

"My dear child, I am happy to present our great national poet, Monsieur Alexander Pushkin. Monsieur Pushkin, this is Mademoiselle Natalya Goncharov."

The girl turned her long neck with the graceful slowness

of a swan. Her curved lashes rose, revealing eyes that were dark and moist. She bent her head shyly, without smiling. The name of Pushkin obviously meant nothing to her.

Despite her bare shoulders, there was about her an inexpressible atmosphere of chastity, something cold and transparent that enveloped her like a halo, that enclosed her like a block of crystal. So much beauty, together with her exquisitely modest expression, gave this child of sixteen an air of majesty.

Pushkin felt every instant binding him more firmly to her young face—the face of a Florentine madonna. He felt powerless to turn away his eyes, haunted by that ineffable profile. Nothing in life mattered any longer, except those unsmiling lips, that soft white forehead, those startled eyes. The most exalted comparisons—flower, bird, star—died on his lips before so much living perfection.

Finally he decided to ask her to dance. She gave him her hand, still with the startled, slightly stern expression that went so well with her curved lips. The irresistible Pushkin, the seducer, the man of a hundred mistresses, the new Casanova whose adventures deliciously horrified the ladies, was troubled to sense a smooth cheek so close to his lips, to embrace a body whose graceful form was no longer a girl's and not yet wholly a woman's.

The music stopped. He took her back to her mother, clicked his heels. She bent her head imperceptibly.

Alexander went out onto the balcony to hide his emotion. The sky was deep and black and powdered with stars. Below, the coachmen, stamping their feet, waited for their masters to leave. His temples hummed. Through his thin dress clothes he did not feel the icy breathing of the night. He was still full of that ineffable image. He had made up

his mind: tomorrow he would present himself officially,
ask for Natalya Goncharov's hand. What did his freedom,
his life of adventures, matter, compared with the possession
of this matchless woman?

A few feet away, in the embrasure of a window, two men
were talking, with glasses of champagne in their hands.
One of them—tall and fat, with a sensual mouth, little cynical eyes, and an extraordinary embroidered waistcoat—was
Sobolevski, the greatest gourmand in St. Petersburg. The
other, the famous Tanzmeister Weber, who was giving the
ball, was short, slight, and looked like Voltaire.

"Madame Alyabiev is still the real queen of the ball,"
said Sobolevski, who was a great amateur of feminine
beauty.

"You are wrong, my dear fellow. The real queen of the
ball is now Mademoiselle Goncharov."

"How so?"

"She has just bowled over the two most famous men in
Russia."

"And they are?"

"The Czar and Pushkin."

ii

For fifty years English and Dutch ships had been coming
to St. Petersburg for raw flax, which went to the spinning
mills in Rotterdam, Glasgow, Hamburg, and Le Havre.
For half a century Europe's sheets had been growing in
Russia's flax fields, and no one had yet realized that instead

of selling hemp, flax, and tow Russia could sell rope, sails, cambric, fine damasks, just as no one had realized that it was only necessary to sow wheat in the black soil of the Ukraine to make it the granary of Europe.

In 1730 spinning mills were rarities in Russia. Nevertheless the raw material stretched away to the horizon, swayed gently under the wind like an immense green sea. Labor swarmed in the wretched villages. A spark of energy and initiative would suffice to start wealth jumping between those two poles.

Ivan Goncharov started the spark jumping when he established his first linen factory. That was in the Kaluga district, in the middle of the flax fields. Guided by the sure instinct of self-interest, Ivan freed his serfs, thus relieving himself of caring for them when they were too young or too old to work. In a short time the erstwhile cloth merchant became one of the richest men in the district.

Faithful to Peter's policy, Catherine ennobled him.

When he died Ivan Goncharov left his heirs in possession of a flourishing industry, which drained all the flax in the district. "The Linen Factories," his estate, no longer bore any resemblance to a factory. It was a mansion, with columns, servants in livery, stables, and kennels.

For fifty years the race of Goncharov remained a race of builders, hungry for profit, hard on the poor. For fifty years gold flowed into the strongboxes of the Linen Factories. But in the process of being mixed with noble blood the thick kulak blood lost its solid qualities, grew thinner, weaker. The Goncharovs lost the secret of multiplying riches.

Ivan's great-grandson, Afanasi Nikolaievich Goncharov, was already a great lord, skilled in no art but that of throwing money out the window. The gold of a province, drained by three generations of hard and crafty muzhiks, went up in fireworks, flowed away between the fingers of bought women, parasites, stewards. The family domains, as large as provinces, disappeared piece by piece to pay for Goncharov's mistresses, his dogs, his paintings, his bastards, his Boulle furniture, his trips to Paris.

His family life had hardly been happy. His wife, nee Countess Musin-Pushkin, could not stomach his infidelities and left him, half insane with grief. He paid very little attention to his only son Nicholas, who was handsome and shy and took after his mother. At nineteen Nicholas married one of the Empress Elisabeth's maids of honor, Natalya Zagryazhski. Natalya was young and very beautiful and she was being married at the Empress's wish—to get her away from court because she had charmed the Empress's lover, Okhotnikov.

Her father had had her in Paris, by a French grisette—whom he had brought back to Russia with him and married, without taking the trouble to obtain a divorce from his first wife. To everyone's surprise the two wives got on together beautifully and finally came to regard their triangular household as a perfectly natural thing.

Natalya's childhood had been passed in this singular atmosphere. She had inherited a certain vulgarity and banality from her plebeian ancestors and resembled the market woman who was her grandmother on her mother's side. The older she grew the sourer and more despotic she became.

Her marriage turned out unfortunately. When she married the rich and handsome Goncharov, heir to the famous Linen Factories, could she know that twenty years later she would not have money enough to pay for resoling their daughters' shoes for their first ball? Could she know that the romantic melancholy that veiled the eyes of her bridegroom was a sign of a terrible mental disease, inherited from the mad countess? The white-haired man with bloodshot eyes who lived locked in the garret, the raging maniac who flung himself on her to bite her nose, was the handsome husband she had married twenty years before.

Her children were no consolation to her. Dmitri, the eldest, stuttered and was deaf; Catherine was too tall and too thin; Alexandra squinted. Only Natalya, the youngest girl, was an accomplished beauty, as if Nature, having tried her hand on her brothers and sisters, had finally produced her, dark and sweet like a Raphael madonna.

So it was absolutely necessary that Natasha should make a brilliant marriage and restore its old luster to the house of Goncharov. Before she was sixteen she was introduced to society in Moscow, the famous marriage market to which girls were brought from the four corners of Russia.

With the five hundred rubles that Grandpapa Goncharov had sent (he certainly owed them that much—he who gave his mistresses ten thousand rubles for a marriage portion, thought Mrs. Goncharov) they had ordered three white crinoline dresses made. That was what was being worn. Shoes and gloves would have to be borrowed from friends. Everyone in Moscow knew about it. Mrs. Goncharov still blushed at the thought. But Natasha, her shoulders bare in her "Venetian" dress, attracted a great deal of attention at her debut. . . .

And now her hand had been formally asked in marriage. For two years they had lived in expectation of this blessed moment; yet Mrs. Goncharov could not make up her mind.

The young man had met Natasha at a ball. Almost the next day Count Tolstoi had come on behalf of Alexander Sergeevich Pushkin to ask for Mademoiselle Natalya Goncharov's hand.

A great writer—well, it was something so different from what one expected for one's daughter, so unlooked for. . . . After all, who was this Pushkin? An author, a man who wrote for the papers. It was true that he was said to be very famous, but fame is not worth a thousand souls and a hundred thousand rubles a year.

And then, can a man of letters be at the same time a man of the world? A poet . . . She would have preferred a substantial man as a son-in-law: a minister, a governor, at least a councilor. With Pushkin, Natasha would not even have a title to put on her visiting card. There were Pushkins who were counts. But not this Pushkin—he was not even a baron. Natalya Pushkin—just that, like a woman of the bourgeoisie.

Did he at least have money? They heard that he was well paid for his verses, but that was certainly a most peculiar source of revenue. As for his position, the less said the better: a man whom—it was common gossip—the police kept under surveillance, a Jacobin, a Decembrist, a revolutionary who spoke ill of the late Emperor Alexander. And then he was credited with several mistresses; his adventures kept the fashionable scandalmongers occupied. No, certainly Pushkin was not a particularly brilliant match. . . .

Yet she had not said no. The season was ending, and if Natasha had plenty of adorers, none of them had yet officially asked for her hand. A poor and beautiful woman was a burden that few young men were anxious to assume. The summer would pass. In the autumn they would have to come back to Moscow where living was so expensive, they would have to order three new ball dresses, answer invitations, pay calls. Under the circumstances it would be better to keep a fiancé in reserve, to fall back on in case of failure.

So she answered evasively: "Natalya is too young, we must wait, be patient. . . ." The following day she received a strange, ardent, highflown letter, and learned that Pushkin had left for the Caucasus that night:

It is upon my knees, and shedding tears of gratitude, that I should write to you, now that Count Tolstoi has brought me your answer: your answer is not a refusal, you permit me to hope!

Yet, if I still murmur, if sorrow and bitterness are mingled with my happy feelings, do not accuse me of ingratitude. I understand a mother's prudence and tenderness. But forgive the impatience of a heart that is sick and intoxicated with happiness. I now take my departure, carrying in my very soul the image of the celestial creature who owes her birth to you. . . .

Natalya Ivanovna shrugged her shoulders, put the letter away, and thought no more about it. Poets and their passions, she decided, were quite past her comprehension.

The object of all this interest, Natasha Goncharov, went on living the life of a marriageable young lady. She had no voice in the matter; neither her hand nor her heart was hers to dispose of. Besides, she would not have known what to do with them.

Life was not gay. They were short of linen and silver and servants; she wore a dress for two years, long after it had gone out of fashion; she got up at dawn; there were long prayers in the morning, in the evening, at meals, and all the while she prayed she must keep her eyes fixed on the corner where the icons were. Even when she went out, there was Mama to see that she did not have too good a time. Mama would not let her speak to gentlemen, or waltz, or drink champagne. She had only one ball dress, and her gloves had been mended.

The days passed slowly in the uncomfortable old house that had not been altered since the end of the century. Sitting on the high-backed sofa—its Empire-green Utrecht velvet cover was worn bald where you rested your back— Catherine, Natalya, and Alexandra spent their afternoons embroidering in the drawing room. It was a long cold room (to save money, they had no fires), its walls decorated with a material so old that it crumbled, and with a full-length portrait of the Emperor Alexander in a general's uniform.

The clock struck twice, then three times, then six and seven times; the strokes dropped into the heavy silence. From time to time, through the ceiling, they heard a wild cry and the furious pacing of a caged beast; that was Papa, trying to open the door of his room. The girls went on embroidering. Catherine was tall and thin, with a yellow skin and black eyes; she looked like a gypsy. Alexandra's features recalled her ineffable sister's; but in Alexandra's face Natalya's romantic pallor was only a dull complexion, and the imperceptible asymmetry that gave such charm to her beautiful sister's eyes was frankly a squint in Alexandra's.

Both Alexandra and Catherine were attractive, but framing—as they always did—their sister's luminous beauty, they looked like two candles flickering in full sunlight. Catherine, who was envious, disliked Natalya for it. Alexandra had resigned herself and loved her sister.

When the girls heard of Pushkin's proposal Catherine bit her lips and said: "It's simply not done. Elder sisters have to be married first. And anyway, I should prefer a soldier, because of his uniform."

"I should like to marry a poet," said Alexandra dreamily.

Natasha did not speak. Pushkin meant nothing to her. She did not read poetry; indeed, Mrs. Goncharov forbade her to read anything except *The Lives of the Saints* and *The Book of Etiquette*. But she would have married anyone at all to get away from her father's house.

iii

There was fog on the lake every morning and the birds flew low, twittering, over the still, heavy water. The birches, touched by autumn, shivered in the wind and waved their delicate yellow crowns with feminine grace. Every morning the puddles were covered by a thin coating of ice that crackled underfoot. It was a Russian autumn, the brief autumn of the North, with melancholy skies crossed by V-shaped flights of storks.

Boldino, a part of which Sergei Lvovich was giving him on the occasion of his marriage, was the family estate of the Pushkins, as Mikhailovskoe was the family estate of the Hannibals. His marriage . . . On August 31, just as he was leaving Moscow, he had written to Natalya:

I am leaving for Nizhni, uncertain of my fate. If your mother is resolved to break off our marriage and you to obey her, I shall subscribe to all the motives that she may give for

*doing so, even if they are exactly as reasonable as the scene
she made yesterday and the insults that it pleases her to
lavish on me.*

He had loved Natalya now for two years, and their stormy
engagement had been going on for six months. In Mrs.
Goncharov's eyes he was not, he knew, a very brilliant
match. In her heart she was still reluctant to give him
Natasha. Otherwise, what explanation was there for the
scenes, the financial scruples, the endless delays? Natalya
Ivanovna behaved like a fishwife, endlessly throwing in his
face all the gossip she had picked up on the subjects of his
gambling losses, his mistresses, his political and licentious
poems. His free life of adventures acquired a sickening
flavor of debauchery and scandal on the old woman's lips.

She kept dinning Natalya's trousseau into his ears—the
impossibility of finding money to pay for it, the disgrace it
would be if she were to be married without one. . . . Her
trousseau? What did he care about her trousseau? What he
wanted was Natalya—without a stitch, if need be, but *now.*

Finally, exhausted, his nerves jangling, he had set out for
Boldino, leaving the door "wide open."

There he was imprisoned in the village by the cholera
epidemic, having no contact with the outside world except
through letters, in which the authorities punched holes to
show that they had been passed. Imprisoned for how long?
There was no way of knowing.

The cholera epidemic that had been ravaging the East
for five years had crossed the Urals and was inexorably moving westward at about the rate of a man traveling on foot.
Fourteen quarantine stations separated Boldino from Moscow, making a barrier that it was impossible to break
through.

He spent whole days in the woods, letting the reins lie on his horse's neck, plunged in reverie, the branches stroking his face as he passed.

He remembered his first proposal, made almost the day after the ball where he had seen Natalya for the first time. A day after receiving an evasive answer he had set out for the Caucasus, because he could not bear to be in Moscow without the assurance that Natasha would be his.

He had gone to Vladicaucasia, Tiflis, Armenia, revisited all that country, which is full of memories as old as humanity, for it was there at the foot of Mount Ararat that Noah landed in the ark.

The Russian Army was completing the conquest of this beautiful land of mountains and water. He was present at the taking of Erzurum, the last Turkish fortress, and passed again over the road he had traveled ten years before with Maria Raevski. Where he remembered steaming water flowing down stony slopes on which it left reddish stains, he saw villas, sidewalks, geraniums in the windows. Civilization had passed that way.

The journey did not calm his fever. Even Maria's memory, bound up with all these places, could not efface Natasha's ineffable image. He had returned to Moscow, hurried to the Goncharovs'. Natalya Ivanovna received him in bed. He asked to see Natasha. She came—pale, constrained, her eyes lowered. A heavy silence fell on them and he fled. All was lost. In the salons he learned that he had a rival: Prince Meshcherski. He was rich, he was a prince, he did not write for the papers. . . .

Pushkin had found St. Petersburg even colder, even grayer, even more geometrical. He gambled and lost enormously. His fame as a poet was only equaled by his current reputation as a seducer. He had mistresses, and even good friends. Countess Zakrevski, a Venus of bronze, beautiful and heavy as a statue, inspired a somber ardor in him. All St. Petersburg was deliciously offended by their relationship. The countess was eccentric and received her visitors in a dressing gown made of transparent lace. Every time she passed before a window you could see her pink legs and the entire architecture of her monumental body. Essentially she was nothing but a hysterical woman who passed from laughter to tears without any reason.

Caroline Sobanska—sister of the Countess Hanska whom Balzac was said to adore—was more interesting. She was beautiful, brimming with wit, and supposed to be a spy. There was Elisabeth Khitrovo too—forty-five years old and in love with him like a schoolgirl. Mrs. Kern, whom he had desired so passionately at Mikhailovskoe, was his mistress also. Too late! It had been an easy conquest and inspired him with nothing but distaste.

Gossip even saddled him with fiancées: Katya Ushakov, a charming frolic who looked like a boy; Anna Olenin, a blond angel with pensive eyes, whose name perhaps he sometimes thought of changing to Anna Pushkin.

But in spite of all this toying with love Natasha's image was there—Natasha in a ball dress, her shoulders bare, the gold *ferronnière* on her black hair; Natasha pale, discomposed, her eyes lowered, giving him her small, trembling hand. At times he would find himself admiring her incomparable beauty, without any sensual desire, almost as if she were a work of art. And then the man of thirty would remember her smooth shoulders, and he would tremble at the image of a slight bride with startled eyes. He felt obscurely that she was pure, not only in body but in mind—

so intensely pure that she seemed transparent. She had never heard of George Sand and had never read the *Physiology of Marriage*, like most other women. She was in no way like the semivirgins of St. Petersburg.

The political situation added to Pushkin's troubled state. After the Decembrist uprising and its tragic epilogue Russia seemed sunk in a heavy sleep. The sympathetic "opposition" of Alexander's days was no more. No one conspired now, no one criticized the government, no one laughed at the police. Everything had become cold and heavy and serious.

Nicholas's reign was a reign after his own image. He had turned Russia into the stronghold of reaction. In France the regime of those who had "learned nothing and forgotten nothing" had been overthrown. Nicholas had unwillingly sanctioned their ruin and recognized Louis Philippe, the puppet king.

In the censored papers there was almost no news of Europe to be found. Europe . . . The desire to see it had become an obsession with Pushkin. Once again he had treated a subject from Russian history in *Poltava*, an admirable poem in which he had followed Byron in narrating Mazeppa's betrayal of Czar Peter and had done it better than Byron. Then he had become interested in the French Middle Ages, with *The Covetous Knight*; and in the deathless Spanish legend, with *The Stone Guest*. Again Paris and its theaters, Germany and its universities, London and its factories haunted his dreams of travel.

Come, I am ready. To fly from the proud girl,
I am ready to follow you, friends, wherever you go.

Were it to the foot of the Great Wall of China,
To seething Paris, or there
Where the nocturnal gondolier no longer sings Tasso,
Where the remains of ancient cities sleep under ashes,
Where cypress groves breathe out odors . . .
Anywhere . . . I am ready. But tell me, friends,
Will my passion die on that long pilgrimage?
Shall I forget the proud girl who is my torment?
Or shall I return once more, to lay at the cruel one's feet
My love, as a sacrifice to her sternness?

To his repeated requests for a passport the government answered no. In any case, something he heard made him change all his plans to travel. He was told that Mrs. Goncharov had spoken of him in kindly terms, had asked to be remembered to him. . . . So Natasha was not engaged to Prince Meshcherski? All was not lost? The next day he left Petersburg without asking General Benkendorf's permission. Three days later, having half killed his horses, he arrived in Moscow, hurried from his post chaise to a ball, and ran into Natalya Goncharov at the door.

They had been engaged for six months. His life of freedom and adventures was to end. Henceforth he would think "we." Thus far happiness had played no part in his life; now he must find enough of it for two.

What was marriage? For some it was shawls bought on credit, a new carriage, and a pink silk dressing gown. For others it was a dowry and a settled life. Until now, all he had known of marriage was jealous thoughts, the difficulty of raising ten thousand rubles, and his mother-in-law's remarks about his bad reputation and Natalya's trousseau.

Natasha herself, now that she had become accessible, had

lost a little of her charm for his versatile heart—the heart of a Don Juan and a poet. And so, when his future mother-in-law's scenes had forced him to abandon Moscow for Boldino, leaving the door "wide open," he had almost hoped that the matter would end there.

"What will happen will be that nothing will happen," he noted on the manuscript of his story, "The Coffin Seller." But prospective husbands did not clutter the streets in Moscow; and taking everything into consideration, Pushkin was not such a bad match. At her mother's dictation, Natasha wrote a note—"sweet but without character"—and Alexander learned that he was still engaged.

He felt sad and moodily poetic, as if it was not to his bachelor life that he was saying good-by but to life itself. The women he had loved were constantly in his mind. Light and charming shadows, they glided into his poems. He had a reputation as a Don Juan, a seducer of virgins. He was Pushkin, the man of a hundred mistresses; Natalya, by his own confession, was his one hundred and thirteenth love. And yet . . .

He sang of love, but ah! his voice was sad.
Alas, he knew of love nought but its pains. . . .

This couplet of Zhukovski's returned to his mind, as in his lyceum days but freighted with a new meaning. . . . He was—not love's master, but its victim, its martyr. His heart could not beat except to love beauty in its every aspect: the beauty of nature, the beauty of art, the warm, living beauty of women. He was man disillusioned, disconsolate, unsatisfied. . . . The women he had loved with a physical love had given him the pox. The women to whom he had brought his soul had given him melancholy in exchange for it. None of the women he had truly loved had loved him in return.

He remembered Katya Sushkov, to whom he had given his heart, his tender, six-year-old's heart, the heart of a budding poet, and who had never given him anything but a piece of gingerbread. Catherine Bakunin, the young lady in black who was looking for a husband . . . One woman especially still haunted him with a strange power, after ten years: Amaliya Riznich, the vampire, the woman with the white neck who had given him every amorous sensation and sent him through all the torments of jealousy. He could see her still, with her heavy black hair, her masculine silk topper with the scarf around it, her big feet concealed under inordinately long skirts. So she had looked when they went driving near Odessa.

She had died in Italy, forsaken by her husband and her lover, carried off in a few months by galloping consumption. He had learned of her death at Mikhailovskoe and felt nothing except remorse for his indifference. Now memories of her were returning and with them regrets:

For the last time I dare to caress your dear image in thought,
To awaken phantoms in my heart, to remember
Your love with a shy and melancholy delight.
I do not evoke you to avenge me upon him who killed my
    beloved,
Nor to learn the secrets of the beyond,
Nor yet because I am still sometimes tortured by doubts,
But because, in my sadness, I would tell you that I love you,
That still I am yours—oh, come to me, come!

"Come to me," he cried, not only to the memory of Amaliya, but to all the women he had received into his heart: Elisabeth, tender and melancholy; Anna Olenin; Zizi, the green fruit of Mikhailovskoe; Pulcheria, placid and beautiful as a mare; and Maria, ardent, grave, unforgettable. . . . And Olga too, the little serf who had been his mistress; Annie with the sad eyes; and Sophia Pushkin, his pretty cousin.

But they had vanished, the charming phantoms of his youth. Maria was in Siberia with her imprisoned husband. Countess Vorontsov—so beautiful, so dreamy—was losing her last youth beside the violet sea. He had heard that she was almost blind. Olga was the illiterate, pregnant woman he had found at Boldino. Her hands were eaten by washing clothes and there were rusty freckles on her face. Sophia, the blond Tanagra figurine, had married Panin, who was wildly in love with her. Pulcheria was married, Zizi was married, Annie was married. . . .

And he was engaged to Natalya Goncharov.

He still had his pen, his faithful old companion. He found it hard to tear himself away from the last chapters of *Eugene Onegin*, the melancholy companion of the past ten years. He felt obscurely that, in Onegin, he had created a type that would endure in Russian literature. And already there was talk about his failing genius, and precisely in regard to the most accomplished stanzas in his entire production!

Until now he had always been adulated and feted. He was beginning to be misunderstood—consequently his genius must be reaching maturity!

On the eve of his marriage his memories of love tore from him verses so beautiful, so melodious, that he sometimes wept over them, his heart gripped by a sweet and penetrating melancholy.

Ten years earlier he had thought that nothing was worth writing but poetry. Now he was trying prose. But what prose! Incisive, so free from artifice that it seemed anatomical, but clear and precise as a diamond. It would have been impossible to take away one word without destroying the whole structure of his phrases. . . .

He had written five tales—attempts at pure narrative, in which for the first time a writer renounced every artifice of his craft and told what he had to tell as briefly and clearly as possible.

The past autumn—spent in the solitude of a village that rose like an island from a countryside infested with cholera and bristling with quarantine stations—had been extraordinarily rich. Pushkin was making haste to store up what he could, as if something were telling him that he should never know peace again.

iv

"My delight, how glad I am to see you!" Pushkin cried, and with his usual impetuosity he embraced Paul Nash-chokin. He had just returned to Moscow after five months of involuntary exile in Boldino.

The cholera was still ravaging Russia. The government did nothing about the terrible scourge except to multiply quarantine zones, thus paralyzing the life of the nation completely. Between Moscow and Nizhni there were now fifteen quarantine stations, and in each of them you had to spend two weeks, living on dry bread, shut up in a peasant *izba* with cockroaches and pigs, in a filth that was quite enough in itself to give anyone the plague.

Paul Nashchokin was a tall blond lad with three passions: his friend Pushkin; his mistress, the gypsy Olga; and a little doll's house a foot and a half high that he was engaged in furnishing. A set of porcelain, which seemed to have been made for a spider, had just arrived from Limoges and he was busily putting the plates away in a buffet of Karelian birch the size of a visiting card, handling them with a pair of tweezers.

"Good morning, my treasure," said Pushkin, addressing the beautiful gypsy girl who lay on a divan that was covered with a Turkish shawl. "Why, are you there too, Tanya?" He kissed the girls on the forehead and sank down beside them. He looked sad.

The gypsies languidly strummed the strings of their guitars, the necks of which were decorated with ribbons. The plaintive notes melted slowly into the clouds of smoke that hung in the air ."Do you know that I am going to get married, Tanya?" Pushkin said slowly. The reddish reflection of a grape-wood fire that was crackling and exploding in the fireplace was thrown up on his pale face and his long black sidewhiskers.

"Do you really mean it, Alexander Sergeevich? May God grant you happiness—you and your wife both. . . ."

"Sing me something, Tanya. It will bring me luck."

"I don't much feel like singing, Alexander Sergeevich," Tanya murmured.

"You don't mean to tell me that you are unhappy in love?"

Pushkin was joking, but his eyes remained sad. The girl sighed.

"We gypsies are never unhappy about anything but love."

"Come on, Tanyushka, sing us something," cried Nashchokin from the corner where he was kneeling before his doll house. "Your lover left you two days ago, Pushkin is getting married next week. . . . It's enough to give anyone a nervous breakdown, on my word of honor!"

Tanya strummed her guitar and began to sing in a warm, throaty voice in whose tones eddied all the heavy melancholy of the dying day:

"Mother, what is that dust cloud, there in the fields?
My lady, what is that dust cloud?
It is horses running away, horses. . . .
But whose horses are they? They are Alexander
Sergeevich's horses——"

Suddenly she stopped singing. An expression of terror came into her face. Pushkin had covered his face with his hands and was sobbing. His slight shoulders shook convulsively. Nashchokin hurried to him.

"Pushkin, what's the matter? What's the matter with you?"

He motioned to the two gypsies to leave the room quietly.

"Come, Alexander, you must tell me what weighs on your heart!"

Pushkin wiped his reddened eyes.

"I must ask you to forgive my weakness. I was feeling sad when I came. Her song upset me. It was not happiness it promised me."

Nashchokin rose and walked up and down several times in silence.

"And you're getting married in that state of mind?"

"I am over thirty," said Pushkin. "At thirty, people marry. There is no happiness except on common paths."

He bowed his head, strummed absently with his fingers. "I expect nothing of life. Happiness would surprise me."

On February 17, 1831, Pushkin buried his bachelor life. There were champagne and toasts and broken glasses, but the atmosphere was neither gay nor happy. The bridegroom-to-be was sad, and his comrades felt a curious constraint about the celebration, which was called a "burial."

The following day, however, was noisy and gay. The marriage took place at noon at the Church of the Ascension. When Natasha, sweet and pale with emotion under her white veil, clutching her round wedding bouquet to her little beating heart, mounted the steps of the church, a sigh of emotion went up from the crowd of spectators.

The ceremony was long and solemn—there was chanting, and tears, and flowers, and candles flickering through the smoke, and the sweet smell of incense. All Moscow had flocked to see such a famous man marry such a beautiful woman.

When, half fainting from the heat and weak with emotion, Natasha raised her veil and offered him her tear-wet face, Alexander felt his heart contract. And the kiss with which he met those lips he had desired so long, their first kiss, of which he had dreamed for two years, gave him only the salt taste of tears.

V

The century-old oaks in the park of Tsarskoe Selo raised their unmoving summits into a pale blue, almost gray sky. For two months the parched earth and the dusty foliage had been vainly asking a little moisture. Every morning a white sun rose in a gray mist that foretold heat. Even the birds had stopped chirping, as if discouraged by the ovenlike temperature.

A squirrel crossed the avenue, climbed a tree velvety with moss, and disappeared among the leaves. Mechanically Alexander followed the graceful little beast's twitching tail with his eyes. These morning walks reminded him of his boyhood. The park was full of memories: there he had looked for the names of his ancestors on a monument erected to commemorate a battle; here he had cried for hours in the tall grass; there his impatient, trembling hands had bared a woman's breast for the first time.

Two months ago he had come here to live with Natasha, his ravishing wife, his angel, his madonna. . . . When evening came she would throw a red shawl over her billowy white dress, tie the strings of her big Milan straw hat under her chin; then, arm in arm, they would walk around the lake. The promenaders would turn to look at a beautiful woman walking with an unusual man. Those who were in the know would whisper: "There are Pushkin and his wife." People called them "Vulcan and Venus."

He had fled from Moscow, his mother-in-law, and family quarrels, hoping that in Tsarskoe Selo he would find the calm that he sought. But not long since, cholera had broken out in St. Petersburg, and the court had taken refuge in the imperial family's summer residence. The yellow façade of the palace had been hurriedly repainted, the lake cleaned, the park trimmed.

And now it was a series of entertainments, hunts, fireworks, excursions. When evening fell they no longer walked arm in arm by the lake. The Czar was too fond of beautiful women; as for the Empress, she bore no grudge against women who pleased her husband, and she had found Natalya charming. Natalya's beauty and that magical name surrounded her with a sort of aureole. She was a great success.

Every evening the crackling of Bengal lights mingled with the thunder that rolled over a rainless sky. Millions of rubles went up in sparks. The light of the fireworks was visible far away, even in the villages where cholera had struck.

The terrible epidemic continued its ravages. All summer it had been hot and dry, as if Nature herself had fever. In places the earth cracked open, like chapped skin. There were forest fires in the South. In Moscow the people, driven mad by the epidemic, chased doctors through the streets. The government had ordered public prayers in the churches; Russia was relying upon God to end the epidemic.

An hour's ride from Tsarskoe Selo the cholera country began. In the cemeteries the gravediggers worked all night by torchlight. Interminable funeral processions crossed the cities at full speed. There were not enough carriages. All hackney coaches had been requisitioned to carry coffins.

But at Tsarskoe Selo the water rippled gently in the marble basins around the sirens' powerful flanks; roses blossomed thickly in the round parterres; there were only the stagnant heat and a vague odor of corpses to recall the scourge that was ravaging Europe.

Pushkin was roused from his reverie by a slow, regular sound like the footfalls of a statue. An instant later he was face to face with the Emperor. Nicholas had not changed. He was as pale and majestic as ever, and seemed in good spirits.

"Good morning, Pushkin," he said, and gave the poet his large, cold hand. "How is your wife?"

Alexander's eyes were suddenly narrow and gray.

"It is too kind of Your Majesty to take an interest in my poor Natalya. She dances a little too much. Aside from that, her health is good."

"Splendid, splendid! The Empress is tremendously fond of her and wants to see her at court often," said the Czar, who had not observed the jealous light in Pushkin's eyes. And, taking him by the arm, he walked on.

"I don't like to see the greatest of Russian writers without any official post," he said with the confidential air which he sometimes used with perfectly unimportant people and which had given him his reputation for simplicity. "I wish to engage your talents in the service of the country, to give you some useful work to do."

Pushkin bowed.

"I should be happy to serve Your Majesty and my country, sire."

"I know that you are not rich," the Czar went on. (Alexander remembered a remark of the Emperor's that had been reported to him: "Since he is married and is not rich, his pot must be kept boiling." How was the Emperor going to make his pot boil?) "What would you say if I should ask you to write the history of Peter the Great? You would receive a salary of . . . let's say five thousand rubles a year."

"Oh, thank you, sire," cried Pushkin with an impulse of real enthusiasm. He had been engrossed in history for some time. "May I have free entry to the archives, sire?"

In a state in which, from peace treaties to the most minor official forms, everything was secret and in which, for fear of publicity, ministerial documents were composed in a special language that it took years of practice to learn, permission to consult the official archives was a serious matter. The Emperor reflected. Should he grant it to this disquieting poet who was still under suspicion? Natalya's black curls passed before his eyes. He smiled imperceptibly.

"In that case you would accept the post I have offered you?"

"Oh yes, sire—and how gratefully!"

"Very well," said the Czar without giving him time to reflect, "then the matter is settled. Come to see me one of these days. We'll talk about it in more detail."

He moved away, heavy and erect, with the gait that was like a statue's. Alexander was left alone. He thrust his hand thoughtfully into his coat and started walking. Until now the Czar's favors had always proved to be forms of servitude.

Suddenly he stood still.

"Could it be because of Natasha?" he said half aloud.

vi

Miss Alexandra Rossetti, maid of honor to the Empress, kissed Natalya on the forehead, sank into an armchair, took off one glove, and fanned herself with it.

"Is your husband at home?" she asked, fixing the young woman with her immense black eyes.

Natalya was embroidering, sitting on a low chair. She answered, pouting:

"Yes—what do you want with him?"

"Jealous?" said Alexandra calmly. "You know that I am no more in love with Alexander than he is with me. What possible harm can it do you if I go up and listen to him recite?"

"He is always telling *me* that such things are outside a woman's sphere," said Natalya, still pouting. She was charming, wrapped in a long snowy dressing gown that left her long slim neck and her white arms free.

"And there's the best possible proof that he doesn't regard me as a woman," Alexandra explained. "Come, don't be silly, Natalya." She rose. "I am going upstairs to see your husband."

She quickly told the rosary of the stairs and entered without knocking. Pushkin, his curly hair wet from his morning bath, was lying in a high-backed chaise-longue, so deep that his slender figure looked frail in it. A bottle of raspberry water stood on a manuscript book of poems within reach of his hand.

"Good morning, my treasure," he said, half rising to kiss

her hand. He was fond of this court *demi-vierge* with her madonna eyes and her boyishness. Beside her Natalya, beautiful and silent, seemed insipid. The Emperor called Alexandra by her first name, Zhukovski and Vyazemski discussed literature with her. Gossip credited her with several affairs. She was more than eccentric—she even spoke Russian in drawing rooms. She said, "To the devil with him," "That stinks like onion," and asked for a second helping of soup at official dinners. She was one of the few women with whom he could talk literature. She came every morning to listen to what he had written the night before.

While she undid the ribbons of her Vandyke bonnet he drank a glass of water and began to read.

Left alone, Natasha resumed her work. She was too shy to feel hatred. In her narrow little heart—the heart of a pretty woman—there were only respectable and lukewarm feelings. Her jealousy was little more than envy.

Fundamentally—she knew it herself—she was only a young lady from Moscow, no longer naïve, lost in the brilliant world of the court. All that she had with which to hold the great man she had married were her black eyes, her white skin, and her slim waist. But under the soft waves of her black hair there was a small brain, incapable of anything but mediocre, everyday thoughts. Her vocation was to be queen of the ball. Like a great many pretty women, she was rather stupid.

Sometimes she longed for Moscow—its alleys that ran nowhere, its courtyards planted with limes, its badly paved streets, its sleepy look. . . . Everything had happened so suddenly. One day this man who frightened her a little and who had never once kissed her all through their long engagement had become her husband. Instructed in the horrifying secrets of marriage before being delivered up to him, she lay like a beautiful corpse between the arms that passionately embraced her—white, her eyes closed.

This beginning of her marriage had left her with terrible memories. Alexander had left her the morning after their wedding night to meet a group of poets and had returned to find her in tears in a house where everything was strange to her. The mournful predictions of the Moscow gossips— "Poor little one!" "So young, so inexperienced, and he so flighty, so egotistical!"—seemed to be coming true.

She took her role of Lady Byron very seriously and, when she appeared in public with her husband, looked pale and melancholy and utterly weary. Dark shadows under her eyes were becoming to her. . . .

The Drama

ON SEPTEMBER 21, 1833, A heavy traveling berlin with drawn blinds drove through the little town of Allenstein, making a great clattering on the uneven pavement, washed clean by the last rain. It stopped in front of the inn, which—like all the inns in all the little towns in Germany—was named At the Sign of the Golden Star, *Zum Goldenen Stern*. Herr Stockmayer, the Golden Star's proprietor, came running with a footstool and helped out a tall thin man wrapped in a traveling cape whose numerous tippets made him look hunchbacked.

"How long will it take to repair the carriage?" the man said, addressing the coachman.

"It will be two or three days before it is fit to travel again, Your Excellency."

When he heard the "Your Excellency," the innkeeper took his long black pipe out of his mouth and removed his cap. The man swore.

"Be good enough to step inside, Excellency," said Herr Stockmayer. "Lieschen, Anna, prepare the room on the second floor facing the street."

The traveler angrily threw his gloves on the table and took off his traveling cape, without which he appeared even taller and thinner. He had a round beard that framed his face but left his cheeks, his chin, and his upper and lower lips bare.

"I should like some dinner," he said in correct but heavy and gutteral German. Herr Stockmayer ran to the kitchen. When he returned the traveler had already emptied a tankard of cold beer. He had reconciled himself to the idea of spending two days in this little Prussian village—as clean and as boring as a Protestant paradise—and seemed in a better humor.

"Have you any other travelers here?" he asked absently, drumming on the table with his long bony fingers.

"No, Excellency, it's a quiet place here at this time of year. You are the only one, except for a Frenchman, a poor young fellow—*ein armer Kerl*—who has fallen ill. I keep him here mostly out of sympathy, Excellency, because he doesn't look as if he had much money."

"A Frenchman, you say?" asked the man with sudden interest. "I should like to see him. Will you ask him if I may pay him a visit after supper?"

The innkeeper touched his cap. Through the window he had seen the traveler's companion, who seemed to be his valet. "Ho there, friend," he called; and when the other had neared, "Who is your master," he asked in a low voice.

"Baron van Heeckeren de Beweerwaard, ambassador from the Netherlands to His Majesty the Czar," answered the man loftily, as if he were own cousin to His Excellency. "We are returning to our post in St. Petersburg."

"Aha," said Herr Stockmayer, and nodded his head as if he had just learned a state secret. Then he ran to execute the traveler's orders, for it was not every day that he had an ambassador in his house.

Left alone, Baron van Heeckeren went to the window, still drumming with his fingers. A Frenchman in this far-away corner of Prussia? France was connected in his mind with his youthful memories. He had begun his career at fifteen, as a sailor in Napoleon's service; Toulon had been his first port. His youth . . . Now he was forty, an old man. But his ambition was satisfied. Ambassador—that was a title worthy of the venerable name of Heeckeren van Beweerwaard.

In 1815, after centuries of servitude, the Netherlands had finally recovered their independence. Beginning as an embassy secretary, then becoming chargé d'affaires, in 1826 the baron was already Netherlands ambassador to Russia. He had the reputation of being the only man with brains, except for the Austrian ambassador, in the St. Petersburg diplomatic corps. When he set out on the leave from which he was now returning, he had received the Order of St. Anne in token of the Czar's good will. The baron stroked the enameled cross that hung from his stock and smiled. He had a disagreeable smile that disclosed his much decayed teeth and gave his long face with its frame of thin hair a cynical look.

Supper was served. He yawned. What a misfortune, this accident to his carriage! He had been too long away from St. Petersburg, from his huge house with its paintings, its porcelains, its antiques that were the despair of other col-lectors. A certain atmosphere of the great world, composed of intrigues, calumnies, and polite lies, was indispensable to him.

He ate with a good appetite and sent for the innkeeper. "May I see your French guest?"

Herr Stockmayer asked him to follow him. They went upstairs.

A fine, pale hand moved aside the bed curtain and Baron van Heeckeren saw a young man of twenty rise with an effort to greet him.

"You are ill, monsieur?" he said in perfect French, although the same blurred accent was discernible in it. "Pardon my curiosity, but our host has told me that you are French. I have a great love for your country, I know it well. . . ."

In the baron's small gray eyes there dawned an emotion in which there was something more than pleasure at seeing a young man who was a native of a happily remembered country. His long sea voyages had taught him to look for beauty in the slim, muscular bodies of young men. This young man was a blond adolescent with blue eyes, and the purity of his profile suggested a Greek vase. A mustache the color of scorched bread marked his upper lip. The baron sat down.

"I hope that my visit will not fatigue you too greatly," he said while his keen eyes traced the slim figure.

"Thank you, I feel much better already. But to whom have I the honor . . . ?"

"Baron van Heeckeren."

The sick man stretched out his hand. "My name is George d'Anthès."

"French?"

"Alsatian."

"Would it be indiscreet to ask where you are going?"

"Not at all. As soon as I have recovered a little strength I shall resume my journey, which will take me to Russia."

"To Russia?" cried the baron, and he looked curiously

at the young man whom Providence seemed to have placed in his path. "Forgive my emotion," he said, "but it is to Russia that I am journeying myself. Allow me to present myself more fully." The baron rose and, clicking his heels like a German, announced: "Jacob Theodore Borhardt Anne van Heeckeren de Beweerwaard, ambassador from His Majesty the King of Holland to the Czar."

D'Anthès bowed, impressed.

"I have some influence with His Majesty the Emperor Nicholas," the baron went on (by force of habit, his hand just touched the Cross of St. Anne). "I should be most happy if I could be of any service to you."

"I have a letter of introduction from Prince William of Prussia, addressed to General Adlerberg. I hoped, by means of it, to enter the service. In addition I am distantly related to the counts of Musin-Pushkin, through my mother the Countess Hatzfeld. But I am certain that your protection would greatly facilitate my approach to the Emperor."

The baron rose.

"It is late, I fear to tire you. Tomorrow we shall talk again at leisure. If necessary, I shall wait for you to recover before resuming my journey. Meanwhile rest and regain your strength."

He took the young man's hand, held it for a long moment, and withdrew.

George d'Anthès lighted one of the thin pale cigars he habitually smoked and threw himself back on the pillow. He must think. Once again his star had sent him the help he needed. When he was a child people had said that a good fairy had left the best of all gifts in his cradle—the gift of charm.

What gave him his charm was not only his blond hair,

his blue eyes, his flame-colored mustache, his broad shoulders, and his slim waist; it was also a certain sweetness in his expression, a well-bred vivaciousness, a ready smile, a light and sparkling wit, a trace of Parisian slang that compensated for his harsh Alsatian accent.

The cigar calmed his nerves and disposed him to reverie. He thought of his childhood, of Soulz, their estate in Alsatia, on the frontier between two countries. It was a huge, severe mansion with a staircase of pink Vosges stone and a gray tile roof where storks nested.

His ancestors had built the old manor house as solidly as they had built their fortune. They were important bourgeois, recently ennobled and still keeping the solid virtues of their kind.

Landholders and builders, they bought land, built factories, sank mines.

His father, Joseph Conrad, was Baron d'Anthès and a member of the Chambre Introuvable. In June 1791 he had helped Louis XVI to escape. Alas, the King got no farther than Varennes! Two years later the baron, a refugee at Coblenz, learned that the Parisians had cut off the King's head.

He was one of those men of whom it was said that they were more royalist than the King, even when the King was named Charles X. After the revolution of July he returned to Soulz, embittered and ruined. For him the son of Philippe Egalité was no king, the dynasty of July was a caricature of a monarchy.

He had an income of twenty thousand livres, debts, and eleven children to support, six of his own and five of his sister's, the widow of the Conte de Belle-Isle.

George sighed. The Revolution had reduced his chances

of a successful career to nothing. The eldest son of Baron d'Anthès could not serve Louis Philippe. At the St. Cyr military academy he jeered the Tricolor and demonstrated in favor of the Duchesse de Berri. Finally he left without finishing his course. It seemed better to seek his fortune in a foreign country. To serve a real king—whether Russian or Prussian—was more honorable than to bear arms under a man whose scepter terminated in an umbrella.

Through his mother, Countess Hatzfeld, he was half German. He went to Berlin. But William of Prussia offered him only the rank of a non-commissioned officer. He was advised to go to Russia. The Czar was reported to be well disposed toward French Legitimists.

And now here he was, his journey not half accomplished, sick, abandoned by everyone. What did the future hold for him—the future that he carried in his breast pocket in the form of a letter of introduction to a Russian general?

He stretched. His cigar had gone out and was exhaling a disagreeable odor of cold ashes. Bah! Providence, which had sent him this round-bearded Dutchman, knew what it was doing. He felt his forehead. He had no more fever. In a week I'll be up again, he thought, and fell asleep.

ii

On June 25, 1834, His Majesty Nicholas I, Emperor of All the Russias, rose early, attended the solemn service celebrated in the church of the Anichkov Palace, and then was to appear in the throne room to receive the congratulations of his courtiers, his ministers, and the diplomatic corps. Such was the procedure laid down by the protocol for imperial birthdays.

The gilding of the great white room glittered in the sunlight. Blank charges, fired from the cannons of the Peter and Paul Fortress, set the crystals of the great pear-shaped chandelier tinkling faintly. The ladies (the Czar, who liked uniforms, had introduced a court costume for them, inspired half by the *Courrier des Modes* and half by the old Russian dress worn by the *boyarinas*) whispered and moved their fans, for their velvet dresses trimmed with fur made them uncomfortably hot.

At last the Emperor was announced. He appeared, very tall and straight, his chest well up. He did not share his brother Alexander's taste for simplicity. Nicholas's Russian and foreign orders formed a solid panoply on his chest, a metal breastplate on which the sun glittered in points of light. One hand rested on the gold pommel of his sword, the other held a two-cornered hat decorated with white plumes. He was the image of majesty.

The orchestra, installed in a balcony, began the Russian anthem—slow, solemn, almost religious. The Czar waited for it to end, standing framed in a doorway through which the long procession of his suite could be seen.

He was fond of such theatrical displays and was always willing to be adored in public. Indeed, with his majestic bearing, his large chest, his long clean-shaven face, and his steady eyes, he seemed to have been created to play the part of an idol.

Finally the anthem ended. Ladies, ministers, diplomats, and courtiers were standing in two rows, one on either side of the room. The Czar moved forward. He walked slowly, with his statuesque gait, setting the soles of his feet heavily on the parquet floor. His face expressed satisfaction.

He was thirty-eight. Though he had reigned less than ten years, his court was one of the most brilliant in Europe and he had already successfully waged two wars that had aggrandized Russia. He believed that he had always been able to rise to any occasion. A coward, he had forced himself to enter plague-ridden Moscow.

Fate had not spared him. There had been the uprising, the cholera, and the floods. In 1833, St. Petersburg had been inundated by the swollen waters of the Neva. Boats rowed along the Nevski Prospect. The black and boiling waters bore along trees, roofs, beds, disinterred coffins, the bodies of children. The newspapers said that the Emperor had visited the scene to comfort the stricken population; actually he had stood for a few minutes on a balcony that overhung the submerged quays, holding his plumed hat with one hand to keep the wind from blowing it away.

Now it was all forgotten. He took the credit for it. It seemed to him that he had "checkmated" (he was fond of that word) the flood as he had "checkmated" the uprising. And so it was that, receiving the congratulations of his courtiers on his thirty-eighth birthday, he looked satisfied and self-confident.

Suddenly, passing a group of young men in the uniforms of *Kammerjunker,* he stopped.

"It seems to me that my gentlemen of the bedchamber are not all present," he said. "Yet it is their duty—on their Emperor's anniversary."

His eyes became hard. He drummed his fingers on the pommel of his sword—a sign of nervousness. A long and terrified silence fell. At last the Czar broke it.

"Where is Pushkin?"

"He reported that he was ill, sire."

"Very well, if he is ill I shall send him my doctor. Arendt! Where is Arendt?"

A search was made for the imperial family's doctor. Nicholas moved on, followed by a scarlet and congested train of courtiers.

His eyes still looked hard.

"See that Zhukovski is sent to me tomorrow morning after breakfast," he said.

The following morning Zhukovski entered the Czar's study and stopped just inside the door, waiting for the storm. He was a mild, goodhearted man, attached to his family, his friends, the czars, and his country. He could not understand how anyone could rise against authority.

In literature he was a revolutionary: he liked Byron, Ossian, and folk poetry, and preached a revolt against clichés and the grand manner; but in private life he was a perfect courtier. For many years he had held the office of tutor to the imperial children. The Empress was fond of him. Pushkin was one of his friends, and Zhukovski was credited with being his protector at court.

The Emperor at last raised his head.

"Oh, so it is you, Zhukovski," he said. The occurrence of the previous day came back to him. "Perhaps you can explain to me why Pushkin did not come to offer me his congratulations yesterday, as it was his duty to do."

Zhukovski bowed his head. He was not fond of lying.

"Sire," he said, "Pushkin is extremely sorry that he gave any appearance of lacking in respect for Your Majesty. The fact is that he is quite ill. Yesterday I found him in bed."

Nicholas exploded. "Nevertheless it is extremely curious that every time there is a ceremony at court there is an illness, a death, or a sudden departure in the Pushkin family! . . ."

He rose and began to pace the room. Finally he stopped before Zhukovski.

"Do you suppose that I am the dupe of these eternal pretexts? Do you think I am blind? Besides, even if I were, the letter that my police have intercepted and which has been laid before me would be quite sufficient to make this matter clear to me. Pushkin is not satisfied with his position as a gentleman of the bedchamber. He avoids coming to court."

The Czar began pacing again, his hands behind his back. "A subject does not discuss his Emperor's bounty," he cried. "I gave him a position at court; his duty is to fill it. Others would be happy in his situation. But he is always in conflict with the protocol. When he is supposed to come in uniform he comes in dress clothes, or else he forgets his hat. . . ."

Zhukovski was on the point of answering that Pushkin loathed his "livery," the striped caftan that was worn only by youths of eighteen and which became neither his age nor his dignity. But he restrained himself. It was better not to cross the Czar on the subject of clothes. Besides, in his heart he felt that Pushkin was wrong.

"Your protégé is ungrateful," the Czar went on. "I had him recalled from exile, I gave him five thousand rubles to write the history of Peter the Great. Instead of which he wrote me a history of Pugachev's rebellion. Nevertheless, when he asked for twenty thousand rubles to publish it, I did not refuse him. Finally, I made him a gentleman of the bedchamber, a title that many other men envy. How has he thanked me? By asking to retire, by complaining to his wife about the uniform in which I have 'bedizened' him, by neglecting his duties. . . ."

Nicholas stopped and wiped his mouth. He had said too much. Zhukovski began a timid defense.

"That will do," said the Czar. "I will overlook it once more, but let him not try my patience further."

He rose as a sign that the audience was ended and accompanied Zhukovski to the door. Then he went back to his chair and lit a cigar.

Pushkin had long since deserved disgrace. But to send him back to his estate (which, incidentally, was just what he wanted) would be to deprive the court of its chief ornament. Nicholas recalled Natalya Pushkin's delicate figure, her rosy shoulders, her long black eyes, and her shining hair, dressed à la Ninon. His Empress was thirty-five and had prominent collarbones. Vera Nelidova, his favorite, was fat and blond. No one else had that goddesslike bearing, those chiseled lips, those chaste, moist eyes.

He remembered the ball in Moscow where he had seen her for the first time. Then she was still a little thing from the provinces with shoulders that were too scrawny. Since then two children and four years of triumph had made her heavier, more regal, more sure of her beauty, and also more coquettish.

He sometimes went and walked up and down under her windows like a young lieutenant; and afterward, dancing with her, would ask her why the curtains of her room were always closed.

To him, Pushkin was no longer the poet (besides, he had ceased to have any success and the censorship forbade most of his work) but Natalya's husband. He had appointed him a Kammerjunker solely in order to give him an official title, which would permit Mrs. Pushkin to be invited to the intimate soirees at the Anichkov Palace. Naturally this *chin* was the lowest, the one that was given to young men just entering court.

Natalya's resistance inflamed the Czar's desire. When his choice fell on a woman—were she a duchess of the blood royal—she was brought to his apartments the next evening, her face concealed by a veil. Even husbands regarded it as an honor to share their wives with the Emperor of All the Russias. In this respect his reign continued the glorious traditions of seventeenth-century France.

Only this monkey-faced, jealous, subversive poet expected to keep the most beautiful woman in Russia for himself. The Emperor was angry. In his heart he regarded the country and all it contained as his personal property. He would gladly have introduced the right of the first night, for nothing seemed to him more desirable than a pretty woman.

Natalya belonged to him by right. He would have covered her with diamonds like an idol, while Pushkin had not even money enough to pay for his wife's clothes. It was Natalya's aunt, Miss Zagryazhski, an elderly maid of honor of the Empress's, who paid the bill for her clothes.

Nicholas yawned, as he always did when he felt nervous, and rang for a footman. When he was disappointed, displeased with his dogs, his mistresses, or Louis Philippe's policies, he went to see his wife. It was his way of loving her. A footman in a white woolen wig and knee breeches entered and stood by the door.

"Announce me to the Empress," Nicholas said.

iii

The cold, sharp rain that had been falling since morning mingled with the old porous frozen snow to make a blackish mud that squelched under the galoshes of pedestrians. Coachmen warmed themselves by vigorously swinging their arms and pommeling themselves, talked to their horses, and said unpleasant things about their masters, whose shadows sometimes passed before the lighted windows of the second story. Every moment a high-wheeled private carriage, drawn by two, three, or five horses according to the rank and wealth of its occupant, stopped before the entrance, at which stood two lackeys armed with umbrellas. From the carriages emerged men in uniform or in tail coats, pumps, and white trousers, and women whose mantillas flowed down over dozens of yards of lace and frills and moire and muslin.

Suddenly a modest-looking equipage (so modest that the gold-braided Swiss guard hesitated whether to run down and open the door) stopped at the entrance. A strange couple emerged from it: the man, short and slight, in a light gray topper whose hairy surface showed signs of wear, a tired swallowtail coat, black tie, and turned-down collar; the woman, with a regal figure, elaborately dressed, her shoulders bare beneath her black mantilla, which she wore over her hair and under which her black eyes flashed. They mounted the steps.

"Announce Monsieur and Madame Pushkin," said the man.

Natalya stopped in front of a mirror to rearrange her side curls. Alexander glanced at her silhouette, so pink that you could not tell where the skin stopped and the dress began. Her hair, freed from the curlers that had imprisoned it all day, fell over her neck in round ringlets. She wore a deeply cut dress, tight in the waist, billowing with lace and flounced petticoats; in her hair there was an ostrich feather curved closely to the shape of her head.

She had kept the bearing of a goddess. Several child-births had passed over her indestructible beauty without leaving a trace. She had simply grown a little stouter, which became her. Her shoulders no longer had the moving slightness of earlier years. Besides, she was no longer the shy and chaste girl who had shut her eyes in his embrace and hidden her breasts under her crossed arms. She was a "lioness," a woman of the world, spoiled by the adoration of the world, the court, and the Czar himself. In all St. Petersburg there was not a young man who was not a little in love with the beautiful Mrs. Pushkin.

Already people were hurrying up to greet her, to embrace her, to invite her to dance. Gradually Pushkin found himself separated from her by the ecstatic crowd.

He straightened up, smoothed his hair, which did not curl as much as it used to, and noticed that there was a button missing from his coat sleeve. Natasha was a wretched housekeeper. She came home at five in the morning and slept until noon. Their house was dilapidated and they ate badly. He could feel the effects of it. His complexion was muddy, the whites of his eyes were turning yellow.

He put his hand to his right side with a gesture that was becoming habitual. His liver was out of order and, besides, this stupid existence was not one to quiet the bile of a decent man.

The lackeys were already removing the hot greasy stubs of candles from the bronze wall chandeliers and replacing them with fresh ones. A waiter passed with a tray. Pushkin took a sherbet and leaned against a doorframe. All this had ceased to amuse him long ago. At the beginning of their marriage he had re-entered the fashionable world in order to amuse his child wife. He was proud of her beauty, her modesty; her success amused him. He bridled his jealousy—the ferocious jealousy of the Hannibals, which made him shudder and turn pale at the mere thought that one of the men who danced with her was touching her arm, her waist. . . .

But after four years of marriage this attendance at social functions had become a habit, a monotonous daily task. He rose late, his head heavy, and went over old letters or old unfinished manuscripts. For two years he had produced almost nothing except fragments, sketches, literary titbits. Aside from *The Bronze Horseman,* a mysterious poem, full of hidden meanings and dripping with rhymes and thoughts and images (the censorship had naturally forbidden it), there was almost nothing that was worthy of him except his strong, dry short story, "The Queen of Spades."

But even those things dated from the miraculous autumn of 1833, when he had torn himself away from Natasha, from their first-born (little Alexander, called Sashka), from his cares, from his friends—as if inspiration, his inconstant old mistress, had made a mysterious appointment with him.

Since then, nothing. Besides, how could he write? His stomach was upset, his heart heavy, his liver out of order. The public—which is to say, the fine ladies, for who else in

Russia read anything?—liked him less. His verses were becoming too pure, insufficiently "romantic." He did not produce enough and had difficulties with the censorship. His magazine, *The Contemporary,* sold very poorly, in spite of the excellent quality of what it published. The poet of liberty was no longer anything in the world's eyes but the husband of Mrs. Pushkin, the most beautiful woman in St. Petersburg.

His eyes sought her in the crowd of dancers and found her, a pink, whirling blur. She was dancing with a blond officer in the white uniform of the Horse Guards.

It was young D'Anthès, an Alsatian refugee, the adopted son of Baron van Heeckeren, ambassador from the Netherlands. Thanks to the ambassador's high protection, the young man, who did not even know Russian, had been put into the guards at once, with an officer's rank. The Czar had given him sixty thousand rubles a year for his equipment. At the recollection Pushkin could not help saying: "If I had sixty thousand rubles now I would pay my debts, take Natalya and the children to the country, and live there, far from balls and scandal and dressmakers and all this pigsty that is St. Petersburg."

This idea had been haunting him for some time. Alas! Boldino, the sound of leaves, mauve evenings—how far away all that was! He was a court official and the husband of a woman whom the Czar wanted to see often. Besides, he owed twenty thousand rubles, hypothecated on his salary. He was a prisoner of imperial benefits.

Natasha passed, light as air, in a glory of pink lace. He raised his eyeglass to his left eye and looked at her. She was still with D'Anthès. The young officer had been paying her court for some time. But who did not pay court to

Natalya Pushkin? Why was he more alarmed by the young Frenchman's assiduities than he was by the Czar's or Count Sologub's or any young St. Petersburg gallant's? Because he was handsome and gay and French and had blond hair and a fine figure? But could anyone seduce Natasha, his beautiful marble statue? Was there a Pygmalion capable of instilling life into his Galatea?

He thought of their life together and of his happiness, so piercing, so incomplete. No, she loved no one and nothing, except her success, the adoration she inspired, and the facile romanticism of the salons. She was born to rule over all hearts in the factitious atmosphere of a ballroom and to eclipse her unhappy rivals. Even her jealousy, the monotonous and paradoxical feeling that resulted in his no longer being able to say that another woman was charming or intelligent without being immediately accused of infidelity —what was it but the outraged pride of a woman whose beauty was admittedly unrivaled?

He went into his host's study, where cards were being played, and leaned over the shoulders of the gamesters. Cards still exercised their mysterious fascination over him, but he was too much afraid of losing. Gone were the days when he would whistlingly pay for a champagne dinner, and console himself for having been cleaned out by a cheat at some relay station by reading Schiller or *La Chartreuse de Parme*.

Now he had debts amounting to sixty thousand rubles, a wife who was the rage, expenses of thirty thousand rubles a year, and two hundred mortgaged souls as a source of income. Someone at one of the tables beckoned to him, but he made a gesture of refusal.

"Why not?" the player asked.

"I have too many debts as it is."

"What a reason! I have debts too."

"My dear Count, you have three thousand souls in the province of Tula, whereas I draw my revenue from the thirty-two letters of the Russian alphabet."

"Always brilliant, Pushkin," the count cried. But it was no longer the general opinion. Those who had known him full of life and jokes were astonished to see him gloomy, proud, reserved. He no longer danced, no longer paid court to the ladies; instead he stood behind a pillar, yawning, and looked at the dancers.

Was it to keep watch over his wife? He was said to be so jealous, so brutal, a real monster. . . . Indeed all sorts of things were said about that strange family, the Pushkins. For example, that he let his parents starve, that he beat his wife, and that during Lent she had even had a miscarriage as a result of the blows he had given her. . . .

Pushkin turned away, went into a small room adjoining the ballroom, sat down, and yawned. He was bored and in a bad humor. A young officer entered—a white silhouette in the half-light of the little room.

"Go and dance, young man," Pushkin said to him. "This room is for married men," and with a bitter smile he pointed to the hunting trophies that decorated the walls.

Natalya felt light and happy, as she always did on the night of a ball. The dancing had made her warm and she knew that such animation was becoming to her. Sitting in a corner, she fanned herself delicately, smiling, making the little coquettish gestures of a woman manipulating a fan.

It was good to be sitting there beside this handsome young

man who said things that it was not hard to understand: "How pretty you are tonight," or "Pink is wonderfully becoming to your black hair."

When they danced she saw at the level of her forehead a red mouth that said things to make her laugh, and a little blond mustache sometimes just grazed her temple. He had a charming name: George d'Anthès. George d'Anthès—that sounded nice, nicer than Alexander Pushkin, for example.

For the first time she felt moved by words of love. The sweet nothings that he said to her, the lover's commonplaces, all took on new, unexpected meaning. She had seen the Emperor of All the Russias at her little feet. But the white, angular Czar had only succeeded in flattering the vanity that she shared with all pretty women. Whereas when her eyes met the caressing look in those clear eyes, everything became simple and gay.

If Natalya had been capable of reflection, perhaps she would have seen an injustice in the fate that separated her from a man who was young, handsome, and carefree like herself. But the absence of lines on her white forehead was more indicative of a habit of never thinking than of youth. She regretted nothing, had no feeling of revolt; she simply gave herself up to the sweetness that came to her from D'Anthès, to the unknown trouble that touched her most intimate, most feminine strings—the strings that her husband had never succeeded in stirring.

"What are you thinking about?"

She turned her swanlike neck slowly, smiled, and said that she was not thinking of anything—which was true. That was just what was so delicious about being with him— that she did not think of anything, neither of what she owed the dressmaker and the milliner, nor of her children,

nor above all of that horrible thing her husband had threatened her with—leaving St. Petersburg and going to live
on their estate in the country. At that idea she shuddered.
Leave this brilliant life, society, the court that adored her,
to go and shut themselves up in a wooden house that smelt
moldy, among coarse, filthy serfs and elderly neighbors who
cared for nothing but eating and cards? To live without
balls, without magazines from Paris, without dressmakers?

She clutched D'Anthès's hand, as if to assure herself
that he was really there; her frightened eyes wandered over
her partner's white tunic, over the chandelier whose wax-
stained crystals announced that the ball was at an end. . . .
He misunderstood her gesture and imperceptibly pressed
her small gloved hand. She did not resist, she gently sur-
rendered to his mute caress.

Certainly she was a married woman and the mother of
three children. She would never forget her duty. But she
was twenty-six, and the world she lived in hardly set her
an example of virtue. The court swarmed with semivirgins,
deceived husbands, and illegitimate children.

The rights of passion which, the poets said, excused
everything—could they not excuse the handclasps, the fur-
tive kisses stolen on balconies, the declarations whispered
during a waltz, all the small change of love that sufficed to
fill the heart, the imagination, and the senses of Natalya
Pushkin?

iv

The house was full of familiar spirits—the ancient aunts and cousins and other feminine presences which always announce either a funeral or a birth.

Natalya lay in a huge bed with twisted posts. In the half-light admitted by the partly drawn curtains her profile, her black hair, were visible against the whiteness of the pillow. She was sleeping the exhausted sleep of a new mother and did not hear her husband enter on tiptoe, bend over her face, which was still damp with the sweat of childbirth, and kiss her forehead.

Elsewhere in the room voices whispered, doors were opened and shut. "How is she?" Alexander asked. "She is doing well." "And the child?" "It's a little girl." He had just returned from Moscow and had heard the news only as he entered the house.

The maids were carrying out basins full of water, towels stained with blood, all the paraphernalia of childbirth; and he felt the same horror of them that his father had felt.

He could not listen to the cries—like the cries of a butchered animal—that are forced from a woman's throat in labor. That his beautiful, sweet Natasha should be subject to the horrible law of childbed seemed to him almost against nature. But children were an inevitable part of marriage.

He kissed the child, a little girl with her mother's almond eyes, lingered a moment longer by the bed on which lay his angel, his queen, his little wife, his madonna. . . .

As always in the first sleep after childbirth, she was

touching and beautiful—her eyelids, fringed with long lashes, modeling her eyeballs; her face pinched with suffering; the perfect curve of her lips dry and blanched from fever. When he saw her thus he forgot the picture of another Natasha—bare-shouldered, radiant with the envy she aroused, mentally undressed by all the men who flocked around her. He had come very near to hating that image.

He left the room, shutting the door softly, and went into his study. Old Nikita—the same man who had served him first as nurse, then as valet—was making up a bed for him on a divan. He looked at himself in a mirror as he passed and found himself thinner and his complexion muddy.

Yet he was only thirty-six. This life was killing him. He often thought of his two hundred comrades whom Nicholas had been keeping in Siberian prisons for ten years. They were ill fed, watched day and night, separated from their families, forced to perform hard labor in the mines. He was free, married to the most beautiful woman in St. Petersburg, and admitted to the Czar's intimacy. But they had peace in their hearts and a sense of having done their duty; and he dragged his way through the vicious and backbiting world of the court with a bad liver, a wife who was too beautiful, and his coat pockets full of pawn tickets.

Their address was known to every pawnbroker in St. Petersburg. His rings, Natalya's jewels, and even their clothes periodically made long stays in the pawnshops. It was the reverse of the brilliant window dressing of their appearances in society, Natasha's clothes, and her social success.

How many times had he not tried to break through the meshes that imprisoned him? It seemed so easy: resign, pay his debts, go to the country, and work, work, work. . . .

But the Czar would not hear of a resignation that would take Natalya way from St. Petersburg, even his friends talked about ingratitude, Natasha wept, finally it all ended in another loan hypothecated on his salary. The twenty or thirty thousand rubles that represented five or six years of bondage were gone in six months and he found himself in exactly the same position as before.

He put his head in his hands, drew a deep breath. For some time he had had a feeling of oppression; now it never left him. He could not bear noise; sudden twitchings convulsed his thick lips. He rarely laughed.

In March his mother had died. "The beautiful Creole" had faded into an impotent old woman, lying shriveled in a huge bed, regretting her life, which had all been spent in nothing, which yet had gone too fast. She had signed to him to bend over her and had croaked:

"Son, I ask you to pardon me for having misunderstood you. . . ."

"Don't say that, Mama. You were the best of mothers."

Sergei Lvovich had sobbed aloud and wrung his hands as if he were playing the fifth act of a romantic tragedy; it did not occur to him that he was terrifying the dying woman.

To distract her Pushkin had brought his wife to visit her. Natasha took off her bonnet, sat beside the bed, and told of her success in the world. By turning her eyes a little, Nadezhda could see her daughter-in-law's head in its armor of curlpapers. "How pretty she is," she sighed.

Finally she had died. Alexander traveled with the body to the Svyatogorski Monastery and attended the burial. When the coffin was lowered he noticed that the ground was dry and yellow as sand. The monastery graveyard was like a garden, with very white walls and a lush growth of vegetation, such as flourishes in many cemeteries. He thought that it would be good to stay there. The idea of death haunted him, had become the principal spring of his poetry.

He had remained for a time at Mikhailovskoe, thinking that perhaps inspiration would come, as before. But he was not at peace; he wrote only fragments, tales, trifles, could finish nothing. Yet writing was no longer a whim of the moment to him or even a need; it was a way of making money. Sometimes he felt that his genius had truly forsaken him. The papers had been saying so for a long time.

Now he was back again in this pigsty of a Petersburg. Tomorrow he would have to put on his "livery" once more, appear at court, dine out, face the solid matrons' lorgnettes. He sighed and put his hand to his right side.

The letters that had come during his absence made a heap on his desk. He opened them—reminders of debts, insulting letters, a few friendly lines from Pletnev, his publisher, a long fiery epistle from an undergraduate in a provincial college, anonymous accusations written with the left hand with errors in spelling: "You are hereby informed that your wife is deceiving you with an officer. A friend who wishes you well." Well, St. Petersburg was beginning again! . . .

He crumpled the anonymous letter and threw it angrily into the wastebasket. But his mind kept returning to those infamous words, traced in a footman's handwriting. "Your wife is deceiving you with an officer. . . ."

Little by little the abstract word "officer" began to come to life, to acquire color. Now it had a white tunic, varnished knee boots, a blond mustache, and a name: D'Anthès. Natasha and D'Anthès.

Sweat broke out on his forehead. Rage—one of those rages of the Hannibals that had made his grandfather faint —gripped his throat. He choked. So the world's calumnies did not even spare a woman who was lying—an angel of beauty and sweetness—on a bed of pain.

He rose and opened the window. The Northern spring— so violent that it makes vegetation sprout in a few days— entered, with its smell of thaw and wet soil. The Moika, a small, shimmering tributary of the Neva, flowed under the windows of their new apartment. He heard the water running in the darkness with a rippling as gentle as a woman's sighs.

No, no, Natasha was not unfaithful. At the most, she was troubled by D'Anthès's constancy. The constancy of a young, handsome man, whose hair was not gray at the temples, who wore the elegant white uniform of the Horse Guards. . . . And she was young, badly advised. . . . She and D'Anthès were only the instruments of society's revenge. He felt no resentment toward her—only an infinite pity for the flower woman who was created to charm all eyes and who lived not by thought but by sensation, as plants live.

The hound pack of society, which hated him as it hated everything that was not mediocre, hypocritical, and vicious like itself, the cosmopolitan clique of the Heeckerens, the Nesselrodes, the Poletikas, was panting with impatience at the thought of being able to call the greatest of Russian poets a cuckold. It was they who were driving Natasha into D'Anthès's arms.

To know that his dearest secrets were laid bare to the light of day, exposed to the unhealthy curiosity of St. Petersburg's gossiping triflers, was torture to him. His name, a

name that belonged to posterity, dragged in the mud. . . .
Perhaps bets were being made on his wife's chances:
"She'll fall, she won't fall . . ."

It was hell. He pressed his forehead between the palms
of his hands. Suddenly there was a soft, shy knock at the
door. He shut the window, composed his features, and
called: "Come in!"

A white shape glided into the room and quietly closed
the door.

"Oh, it's you, Alexandra," he said.

"Yes, I came to see if there was anything you needed."

"Come here, then. I haven't had a chance to greet you
since I returned."

She came to him.

For a year he had rented this house on Moika Quay with
his two sisters-in-law. Catherine, the elder, he did not like;
she was obstinate and stupid and had neither Natasha's
beauty nor her sweetness. He suspected that she was in love
with D'Anthès.

But Alexandra pleased him. She had everything that
Natasha lacked: tact, intelligence, energy. It was she who
looked after the children and the house. She could listen
to him for hours, as another Alexandra once had done, the
dark-haired Alexandra Rossetti.

Natalya plus Alexandra—that was the woman he wanted.
They resembled each other physically and completed each
other morally. Sometimes he thought that they were only
two aspects of the same woman. The ambiguity created a
complex atmosphere, a subtle erotic climate, between Alexandra and himself.

"Sit down, Alexandra."

The girl dropped onto a divan. In the shadows he saw

her white skirt, with the candlelight dancing tremblingly on it. In profile she looked like Natasha; she had the same tall, slight figure, the same pure, classic features, the same pallor that had made their acquaintance give her the romantic nickname of "Pale Angel." Only, when she turned her head, you saw that her black eyes were crossed, you saw all the faults that spoiled the traditional beauty of the Goncharovs in her face.

"Well, Alexandra, tell me all about Sashka. Was he good while I was away? Or does he still insist on asking for everything that you won't let him have?"

He sat down beside her, still talking in the same playful way. She let him continue in silence, half lying on the divan like a forgotten scarf.

Suddenly she looked at him with those dark eyes that were like Natasha's.

"Alexander, you are unhappy. . . ."

He started, wanted to make a joke of it, but realized the uselessness of lying to this woman who loved him; he took her long, pale hand and raised it to his lips.

She made no resistance. She did not understand how anyone, knowing him, could prefer the doll-faced youngster her sisters were both in love with. What were D'Anthès's blond hair, his elegant carriage, his air of a man who knew women, compared with those eyes full of fire and genius, that mouth, once so full of laughter, now drawn and bitter, with lines of suffering marked in the corners?

Deep within her there was an immense reserve of unused tenderness, a thirst to love, to console. She looked up at him with haggard eyes that said: "Take me, hurt me if you will, but stop being unhappy!"

Suddenly it came to him that he was alone with her, that

he had only to stretch out his arm and his fingers would feel the soft elasticity of a woman's breast. The spring air, which he had been finding so soothing, so quieting, suddenly set him trembling with desire. Something in him melted deliciously, awaiting happiness.

He wanted to rise, but in Alexandra's eyes he read such despair, such entreaty, that he returned, took her in his arms, gently bent her slight form back on the pillow. His lips sought and found two other lips—lips that were warm, unskillful, ardent.

The Tragedy

ON NOVEMBER 6, 1836, A HACKNEY carriage stopped before the house of Vasili Andreevich Zhukovski, not far from the palace of Tsarskoe Selo. A young man of about twenty descended from the carriage and knocked at the door of the illustrious romantic poet, tutor to the imperial children. When the visitor was announced, surprise wrote itself on Zhukovski's well-groomed face. He was not especially intimate with the Goncharovs, and a morning visit from the youngest son of the family was something to startle him.

"Vasili Andreich, knowing your affection for Pushkin, I have permitted myself to seek you out in regard to a matter of the utmost gravity. . . ."

Uneasiness appeared on the good poet's face.

"Something has happened to Pushkin!"

"Only your intervention can prevent a calamity. Pushkin's life, my sister's honor, are at stake. My family and I implore you to intervene, to approach my brother-in-law."

"But in heaven's name, what is the matter?"

"Pushkin has just challenged George d'Anthès to a duel."

Zhukovski turned pale, remained speechless for a moment, then rose and began to pace hurriedly back and forth.

"It was certain to happen," he cried, much agitated. "I have been fearing it for a year. And how could it be otherwise? For two years he has been being slowly tortured to death—by D'Anthès with his attentions, by the world with its gossip——" (He was going to add, "by the censors with their chicaneries," but refrained. His long years at court had made him circumspect.) "Poor soul! He, so sensitive, so passionate . . . But how did it happen?"

"Yesterday morning certain of our friends—Khitrovo, Vyazemski, Sologub, and so on—each received through the mail a packet containing a folded sheet of paper addressed to Alexander. Some of them, suspecting an insult and invoking the rights of friendship, destroyed the packet. Unfortunately the same idea did not occur to them all. And so Pushkin received three of these packets, which contained an anonymous 'diploma' in which he was named 'Coadjutor of the Order of Cuckolds.'"

Zhukovski leaped. His nostrils trembled with anger. His look of wrath was ill suited to his usually kind and placid face, the face of a sentimental philosopher.

"What an infamy, what baseness! Ah, how well I recognize their hand in this! They will never rest until they have brought him to ruin. . . ."

Sergei Goncharov rose.

"Vasili Andreich, you have influence over him; he will listen to you. Talk to him, persuade him that this odious joke is not worth risking his life over. . . . Think what Pushkin means to Russia, think of my poor sister, of their children!"

"I am doubtful of succeeding, but there is nothing I will not do to save Pushkin."

Zhukovski rang, and sent for his cape, his cane, and his hat. The two men left the house. An hour later a hackney coachman, who had half killed his thin Rosinante, set them down at Pushkin's door.

They found him calm, almost gay, as if he had just accomplished a gesture of freedom. Only the convulsive tremblings that shook him from time to time expressed the inner agitation of a wounded soul. For the first time Zhukovski noticed the immense weariness expressed by his drawn mouth, the two lines that ran from his nostrils to the corners of his lips; and the older man's heart bled with compassion. He loved Pushkin and had watched him increase in stature and become the national poet of Russia.

Alexander motioned him into his study.

"I do not wish my wife to know anything about this matter," he said, shutting the door. Zhukovski took both his hands.

"Alexander, I beg you, come to your senses, think of your wife! Are you going to drag her name into such a scandal?"

Pushkin tossed him a sheet of paper.

"Read that, and tell me how a gentleman can leave such a thing unanswered."

Zhukovski took the letter. He read:

The Masters, Commanders, and Knights of the Most Serene Order of Cuckolds, gathered in full chapter under the presidency of the venerable Grand Master of the Order, His Excellency D. L. Naryshkin, have unanimously named Monsieur Alexander Pushkin coadjutor to the Grand Mas-

ter of the Order of Cuckolds and Historiographer of the Order.

The Perpetual Secretary: COUNT J. BORCH

Zhukovski trembled. The infamous missive, written in letters resembling print on a sheet of thick white letter paper, must emanate from a man of the world, for it was composed in impeccable French. It came from one who was well informed of court intrigues, for only a man as blinded by jealousy as Pushkin could fail to see that it referred not to Natalya's relations with D'Anthès but to the Czar's assiduous pursuit of the beautiful Mrs. Pushkin.

Naryshkin was the husband of a woman of great beauty, mistress of the Emperor Alexander. Pushkin was the husband of another woman of great beauty, mistress of the Emperor Nicholas.

But what then? Was he to open the poet's jealous eyes, turn his anger upon the sacrosanct person of the Czar? To do so would change nothing. Besides, perhaps Pushkin knew it already and pretended not to have noticed—for what had he, a poor poet in disgrace, in comparison with the most powerful man in Russia, perhaps in the world?

Zhukovski quietly laid down the sheet of paper.

"It is utterly disgusting. But an anonymous letter should be treated with contempt. Besides, what makes you think that D'Anthès has a hand in it? On the contrary, I should suppose it in no way to his interest to anger you in this fashion."

Pushkin leaped from his chair. His lips trembled. The whites of his eyes became bloodshot. The Negroid characteristics of his face were heightened by anger.

"In him I perceive the cause of this calumny. His attentions have given rise to the whispers that have poisoned my life for two years. I am resolved to put an end to it. If I kill him I shall be exiled, and I ask nothing better than to leave St. Petersburg. If he kills me . . . that is a way out too."

He began to pace up and down.

"I have already begun to put my affairs in order. I have written to the Minister of Finance and placed at his disposal my two hundred souls and the village that my father gave me at the time of my marriage. That is more than enough to cancel the forty-five thousand rubles that I owe the Treasury. . . . No more imperial benefits. As for my other debts, I shall look into them later."

"But why break with everything? Why risk your life? We all know that your wife is innocent."

Pushkin whirled round.

"It is not enough for me to know that my friends consider her innocent. My wife is an angel. No suspicion can even touch her. But my name belongs to the country and must be respected wherever it is known. That is why I must either kill D'Anthès or let him kill me. This foul business has gone too far for me to let it drop now. Remember that this letter was sent to eight people!"

He went to the window. Against the light his figure appeared even slighter.

"I have talked to my wife," he said gently, without turning around. "She has told me everything. There has never been anything between her and D'Anthès but innocent flirting. Perhaps he attracts her. He has the qualities that attract women. But she has never forgotten her duty to me. The whole thing has been turned into poison by talk. And besides, that blackguard Heeckeren, who calls himself

D'Anthès' father by adoption, pursues her everywhere, to tell her that his son—so called—is in love with her. . . . He urges her to yield to his puppy's desires."

He broke off. The doorbell had rung. A valet entered and announced Baron van Heeckeren.

"Show him in," said Pushkin shortly.

The baron entered, looking strained and embarrassed. He was tall and thin, with narrow shoulders and a gaunt neck; his small greenish eyes wavered from one object to another. He looked like an old plucked bird.

As he spoke of his paternal feeling for D'Anthès Pushkin listened in icy silence with a look of scorn riveted on his expressive face. The baron ended by sitting down on the edge of a chair, without having been asked.

"All the hopes that I had built upon my son's future are destroyed at the very moment when I thought my work finished. Nevertheless I accept your challenge, Monsieur de Pushkin, for George's honor is more precious to me than his life."

The baron looked furtively at Pushkin to see if this sentence had produced the desired effect upon him. Seeing that the poet remained silent, he went on: he had come without George's knowledge, to obtain a delay. Could Monsieur de Pushkin grant two weeks? George's family and he himself would be extremely grateful to Monsieur de Pushkin. Besides, Monsieur de Pushkin would reflect and would surely realize that there was no reason whatever why this duel should take place, Monsieur de Pushkin and his George being made to understand and esteem each other.

Monsieur de Pushkin granted all that was asked of him,

simply to be relieved of the baron's presence, provided that the duel should eventually take place.

Zhukovski handed the footman his top hat, his silver-headed cane, and his cape, and asked to see His Excellency the Dutch ambassador.

Zhukovski was tired. For forty-eight hours he had been scouring the streets of St. Petersburg trying to adjust this fatal business. Until now his efforts had been vain. Old Heeckeren did not want the duel to take place because it would greatly compromise his diplomatic career and the future of the man he called his son, but at every move he had come up against Pushkin's implacable determination.

Zhukovski glanced around: the embassy looked like a museum. Heeckeren was obviously a man who knew pictures.

The baron entered and Zhukovski took his hand without pleasure. His frank and easygoing nature instinctively recoiled from the tall thin diplomat with his shifting eyes. Heeckeren looked older, as if worn out by anxiety. He had not slept for two days. At any price the meeting must be prevented. The Emperor disliked duels and punished them severely. If George fought, it was all over with his career in the Russian Army, even if he did not kill Pushkin. And he himself, the ambassador of His Majesty the King of Holland—what sort of a role was he playing in all this? Aside from these considerations, there was the danger to his George, the man whom he loved with the mingled feelings of father and lover.

He began to protest his innocence.

"Believe me, Monsieur Zhukovski, Monsieur de Pushkin's suspicions are unfounded. Ab-so-lute-ly unfounded.

His resentful and vindictive nature is leading him into an evil act, an act that he will later regret."

The baron raised his eyes to the ceiling.

"God knows how many times I have warned Madame Pushkin that her conduct was giving rise to gossip." (Zhukovski remembered what Pushkin had said: "He pursues her everywhere to tell her that his son is in love with her, urges her to yield to the puppy's desires. . . .") "How many times have I not pointed out to her the abyss that was opening under her feet! Believe me, Monsieur Zhukovski, I have sometimes carried my frankness to the verge of disrespect. But you know women, particularly pretty women! Can you ask a pretty woman to renounce the triumphs of vanity?"

Zhukovski rose.

"Monsieur de Heeckeren, I did not come here to discuss Madame Pushkin's conduct but to try, with your assistance, to find some way of settling this matter without bloodshed. Your son's arduous attentions to my friend's wife have given rise to the gossip that compels him to demand satisfaction on the field."

"My son's attentions to Madame Pushkin, did you say, Monsieur Zhukovski? Are you quite sure that his homage was addressed to her?"

"It seems to me that Monsieur d'Anthès' passion for Madame Pushkin is common knowledge. . . . He follows her everywhere."

"But it is just there that you are deceived," cried the baron triumphantly. "It is true that George is to be found wherever Madame Pushkin goes, but it is not *her* company that he seeks—it is her sister's, who as you know always accompanies her."

Zhukovski looked at him, flabbergasted.

"Alexandra?"

"No, not Mademoiselle Alexandra. My son is in love with Mademoiselle Catherine Goncharov, Madame Pushkin's elder sister. It was she whom he attempted to see, by appearing wherever your friend's wife appeared. George has already asked me for permission to marry Mademoiselle Goncharov. Until now I have always refused, as I considered the young lady's financial situation too precarious. But in view of the constancy of my son's feelings I should perhaps feel inclined to give my consent—were it not for this unfortunate affair of the duel!"

The baron gave Zhukovski a look that was full of meaning and, as was his habit, caressed the Cross of St. Anne that hung at his neck.

"Let me make myself clear, Monsieur Zhukovski. You are a man of the world: if my son were to ask for Mademoiselle Goncharov's hand now, his action might be attributed to a wish to avoid this duel—a conclusion that I could not permit to be drawn, no matter at what cost. Whereas if Monsieur Pushkin were to withdraw his challenge . . . Do you understand me?"

Zhukovski looked at him, stupefied. So much baseness combined with so much cleverness filled him with a kind of disgust in which there was a certain admiration. Did Heeckeren think him naïve enough to believe this fairy tale about D'Anthès's love for Catherine? The man of the hour, the handsomest Horse Guardsman in St. Petersburg, in love with that broomstick of a Catherine Goncharov, a woman without beauty, without intelligence, without money? But stay—was he to raise difficulties over the means? If D'Anthès married Catherine the duel became impossible. And besides, there would be no reason for it, since the young man's behavior would be justified in the eyes of the world. What was essential was to save Pushkin's precious life. . . . He rose.

"What you have just revealed to me completely changes the aspect of the problem, Monsieur de Heeckeren. I can only advise you to ask for Mademoiselle Goncharov's hand without delay. As for me, I shall go at once to announce the good news to my friend."

He was in a hurry to be gone. Everything had been arranged at the very moment when he had thought that matters were most desperate. The baron put out his hand.

"One word more, Monsieur Zhukovski. I hope that all this will remain between ourselves. Consider that a word, a single indiscretion, may force my son to go on the field. . . ."

Zhukovski bowed.

"You may count upon me to prevent any such indiscretion," he said.

ii

The marriage of Baron d'Anthès de Heeckeren to Miss Goncharov took place in St. Petersburg on January 10, 1837, according to the rites of the Catholic and Orthodox Church. Catherine, pale with emotion and almost beautiful in her happiness, held the tight round bridal bouquet against her heart, just as Natasha had held another six years before as she mounted the steps of the Church of the Ascension.

For two months she had been living in a sort of white

dream bordered with lace. At twenty-six—poor, and odd-looking rather than pretty—she had seen before her the desolate future of an old maid without any goal in life. Happiness had pounced on her and left her stupefied with astonishment. She was not responsible for the happiness that had come to her? Her marriage was only a façade, intended to save the reputation of another woman, and that other woman her own sister? What did such things matter to her? The fact remained. She was engaged to the handsomest, the most sought-after man in St. Petersburg—to the very man whom she had loved for two years without the slightest hope of his giving her anything more than a word, a preoccupied look, a gentleman's courtesies.

Women envied her, men thought of her benevolently, but the general feeling was one of surprise. People felt sorry for D'Anthès—he, so young and so handsome, to be tying himself for life to save the reputation of the woman he loved. Ah! That was chivalrous, that was romantic. . . . It made him even more interesting. The marriage gave all St. Petersburg its only subject of conversation.

All the lorgnettes were turned upon him in the shadowy St. James Cathedral, in which the Orthodox wedding was celebrated. He held a thick yellow candle in his hand; its light shone on his face. In his white uniform he looked like a sacrificial victim.

Now two heavy crowns were being set on the bent heads of D'Anthès and Catherine. . . . They turned their pale faces toward each other and their lips met in the first kiss of marriage. . . . A few sensitive ladies put their handkerchiefs to their lips and shed a pair of ceremonious tears.

D'Anthès felt that he was the center of attention and held his athletic torso—like a cast swathed in white cloth—erect.

Sensitive souls pitied him. Yet he did not feel unhappy. He had courted a married woman. He had been challenged to a duel. Now, instead of fighting, he was marrying. It was simple. He took life as he took a woman—by the waist.

By squinting a little he could see his wife: her eyes were raised to the images of the saints and she seemed to be praying fervently. Was she pretty? Dark, heavy hair, black eyes, a tall, slim figure. She looked a little like Natalya— well, she would bear handsome children. . . .

The two ceremonies ended late in the afternoon. A reception, followed by a soiree, was to be given in the house of the Dutch ambassador. The young couple attended with their guests. There were toasts, champagne, and flowers of rhetoric.

The bride, who had removed her crown of orange blossoms and disposed of her bouquet, danced with her husband, clinging to him amorously.

At ten o'clock there was a sudden eddy. The crowd of guests parted before a woman who was making her entrance. It was Natalya Pushkin. The absence of the couple from the church ceremony had been widely noticed.

Natalya was moved. Her black high-necked dress (the court was in mourning) set off her goddesslike figure and accentuated the pallor of her complexion. She kissed her sister and gave her new brother-in-law her hand.

"I am happy for you," she said, and was sincere. She could neither love nor hate deeply. Her placid soul was made for submission. Assembling Catherine's trousseau had consoled her for the loss of her lover.

D'Anthès asked her to dance and carried her off, a soft, willing prey, in the voluptuous gyrations of a waltz. The sacrifice that he had made for her sake rendered her even dearer and more desirable to him. Gilded panels, the pink blurs that were faces, passed before their eyes in a sort of round dance of which they were the center. They saw neither the perfidious looks of astonishment that followed them nor the sudden pallor of the bride.

They were together again under the chandeliers, the duel had not taken place, and Pushkin was not there. And henceforth the bond of kinship by which they were united would justify a certain familiarity.

iii

On Monday, January 25, 1837, a man was walking up and down in front of the barracks of the St. Petersburg Horse Guards. The Horse Guards were a crack corps whose membership represented the best families in the country. Their barracks, where the officers lived with their families, were very comfortable.

The pacing man was tall, with reddish-brown hair. His long, fur-lined officer's cloak was thrown over one shoulder despite the cold that was turning people's noses blue. Russian officers had a certain number of traditions, one of which maintained that they were never cold enough to button their overcoats.

Men in uniform were going and coming by the great gate of the barracks. One of them stopped and addressed the auburn-haired officer.

"Hi, Lanskoi! Still on sentry duty under Madame Poletika's window? What a troubadour!"

Lanskoi smiled good-naturedly. His passion for his comrade Poletika's wife was known to everyone, including her husband. Mrs. Poletika was a tall blonde, gay and mischievous, who wore her hair in a complicated style and bore the strange name of Idalya. Their frivolous and romantic relationship was one of those that society accepted.

Lanskoi had been waiting for some time when he was joined by a blond officer wearing the white uniform of a lieutenant in the Horse Guards. He looked preoccupied.

"You know what you have to do?"

"Idalya has told me what's in the wind."

"But besides that?"

"I am to keep watch outside her apartment here and give warning if anything suspicious occurs. Don't worry —this is not the first time I've done this sort of thing!" Lanskoi burst out laughing and winked one eye. This fellow D'Anthès, after all! To hook the most beautiful woman in St. Petersburg in the teeth of the most jealous husband in Russia!

He slapped him on the back.

"So she is coming, your Dulcinea—is she?"

"I don't know. I have threatened to kill myself if she doesn't come."

"Hoho! So you're trying desperate means!"

"The means don't count. Only the end matters."

They both smiled simultaneously at the thought of the "end" that was to be enacted behind those blinds, which Idalya had been careful to close before she left her apartment. Because of the coming rendezvous, which had been arranged by Lanskoi's mistress, the freemasonry of successful lovers had sprung up between the two men. They had nothing to hide from each other. Besides, it was the sort of adventure one could be proud to have a share in.

Finally D'Anthès entered and went upstairs. Lanskoi resumed his sentry duty. In his thoughts he followed his friend into the apartment that he knew so well. Idalya would have put flowers in the vases, drawn the curtains, and lighted the lamp with its round opaline shade. The hussy! Why had she undertaken to play the go-between? Out of curiosity? Out of a desire to bring about the fall of the cold and beautiful woman who was her friend? Or was it because she hated Pushkin?

He himself had no liking for that strange, scornful person. After all, who was Pushkin? A journalist, a rhymer. He was received because he came of a good family and because the Czar was in love with his wife.

Lanskoi started to walk back and forth again. Something in his gentlemanly soul told him that all these reasons did not justify his playing a part in an adultery, even if it was only as a supernumerary. But, bah! Everyone knew that Pushkin slept with his own sister-in-law. . . .

At last a hackney coach stopped before the building. A veiled woman alighted. Lanskoi discreetly turned his back. When he turned around again she was no longer there. He resumed his pacing.

Natasha shut the door, dropped into a chair, and began to cry. Over her smooth cheeks tears poured, warm and fast. Behind the door of the study that she had just left she could hear her husband's footfalls. He was striding up and down, as he always did when he was disturbed. The sound of his footsteps, which did not stop for an hour, obsessed her like remorse. She ran into her room, flung herself on the bed, and wept, with her head under the pillow.

When he had sent for her that morning she had instantly

sensed that he knew everything. He handed her a letter. "Read this." But she did not need to read it. She confessed at once: yes, she had gone to the rendezvous. No, she had nothing to hide from him. Didn't she tell him everything? Didn't she even tell him the puns that D'Anthès made up to amuse her? But this time she had feared his anger.

Could she know that D'Anthès's desperate letter—the letter in which he had threatened to commit suicide and to kill Catherine at the same time—was only a lover's trick? Could she know that the rendezvous would be a premeditated ambush, that she would find the blinds closed, the curtains drawn, champagne on the table? That Idalya would not be there, that someone would be watching under the window, that everything would have been arranged to throw her into her lover's arms?

Telling him all her story she wrung her hands, as she had the evening before when she had implored D'Anthès to leave her. It had gone too far. She had thought that it would be nothing but a flirtation. Adultery—that was something too momentous for her timid soul. Then, suddenly, a man's violence, a man's desire for possession, had entered the scene. No, she had not wanted that! But who now would believe that she had resisted, called for help, fled? . . .

Her husband had told her to leave him alone, with a gentleness that was heavy with terrible resolves. And for an hour he had been walking, walking, with the regularity of a metronome. . . .

Night fell quickly, as if in haste to have done. Behind the window there hung a sort of black fog, through which lights glimmered feebly. The Moika, covered with dirty ice, did not make its familiar little murmur under the windows.

He had forgotten to have the fire lighted in his study. Suddenly he became aware that he was cold.

It was enough to make a man knock his brains out. Two months before he had thought that he was finished with D'Anthès. His vengeance had been subtle and deep. He had forced his adversary to marry under threat of arms. People were still laughing over it in the two capitals. If he had killed D'Anthès in a duel, perhaps Natasha would have been left with the memory of a romantic hero, a man who had died to save her honor. Whereas now she could only laugh at the gallant who had taken refuge behind another woman's skirts.

At least so Alexander had thought. But only two weeks after the marriage the whole problem had been reopened. The gay life of St. Petersburg was beginning all over again. Now there were balls twice a day. D'Anthès was still the hero of the hour; his marriage had only added a ray to his halo. He was married, but did that make him any less blond or less gay or less charming? Among his belongings there was a thin, dark woman to whom he would say loudly, "Come now, my legitimate wife!"—that was all.

He was never away from Natalya. Was she not his sister-in-law? Did not his sacrifice deserve some reward? His witticisms—which smelt of the guardhouse—were retailed everywhere. The two sisters had the same chiropodist. "He told me that Madame Pushkin's corn was more beautiful than my wife's," said D'Anthès, playing on the words "cor" and "corps."

Their fashionable flirtation had always been the object of a sort of low, unhealthy curiosity, whose vulgarity was torture to a sensitive and passionate soul. But their clandestine rendezvous was the drop that made the vessel run over. Natasha, his angel, his queen, his dark madonna, in this sickening atmosphere of fashionable adultery . . . The mother of his children lying on a divan that belonged in a risqué musical comedy . . . That picture drove him mad. He sunk his head on his arms and wept. Tears lightened the burden of cold anger that was stifling him.

He felt no hatred against his wife. Yes, he was certain that it had all taken place just as she had described it to him. She had been enticed into an ambush, she had been thrown into D'Anthès's arms. She had committed an error, not a sin. His confidence in her remained religiously whole. He needed to believe in her.

But who? That young pretty-face, whose mustache did duty for an expression? He was only an instrument. No, it was the whole fashionable clique, the Poletikas, the Nesselrodes, all the German and Baltic riffraff who looked to Metternich for orders but with whom the Czar surrounded himself because he was afraid of the Russian nobility who had brought about the Fourteenth of December. . . . And at their head, Heeckeren, the gold-laced blackguard who could not forgive him for those days of anxiety, for that grotesque marriage. Heeckeren, who had urged Natalya to satisfy his "son's" desires, Heeckeren, who, probably, had arranged their rendezvous, as he had sent the "diploma" of November sixth.

He tore off his cravat and unbuttoned the collar of his shirt. The veins swelled on his temples as if he were making a great physical effort. His right side pained him.

But what now? Challenge D'Anthès to a duel? D'Anthès would find some trick to avoid fighting. Well then? He opened a drawer and took out a notebook full of jottings.

The day after receiving the anonymous diploma he had sketched a letter to the Dutch ambassador—a letter full of terrible insults, such as could not be washed out except in blood. At last the letter was to serve its purpose.

MONSIEUR LE BARON:

Permit me to review what has just taken place. Your son's conduct has long been known to me and could not remain a matter of indifference. I contented myself with the role of observer, prepared to intervene when I should consider it proper. An incident which, at any other time, I should have found extremely disagreeable, fortunately occurred to solve my difficulty. I received certain anonymous letters. I saw that the moment had come, and I took advantage of it. You know the rest. I forced your son to play a role so pitiful that my wife, astounded by such cowardice and vapidity, could not refrain from laughing; and the emotion that she had perhaps felt for such a great and sublime passion perished in quiet scorn and well-merited disgust.

I am forced to admit, Monsieur le Baron, that your own role has not been an entirely becoming one. You, the representative of a crowned head, have acted paternally as a pimp for the young gentleman, your son. It would seem that all his proceedings (sufficiently maladroit ones, be it said) have been directed by you. It was you, probably, who dictated to him the sorry things he has said and the nonsense he has undertaken to write. Like an obscene old woman, you have lain in wait for my wife in every dark corner to tell her of the love of your bastard—real or so called —and when, ill with the pox, he was obliged to remain at home, you said that he was dying for love of her; you mumbled: "Give me back my son."

You can well understand, Monsieur le Baron, that after all this I cannot permit my family to continue any relations whatever with yours. It was upon that condition that I had consented to let this filthy matter drop and not to dishonor you in the eyes of our court and your own as I had the power and the intention to do. I no longer care to have my wife listen to your paternal exhortations. I cannot permit your son, after his abject behavior, to address my wife; still less can I permit him to regale her with guardhouse witticisms and to play the devoted and unhappy lover, when actually he is nothing but a coward and a blackguard. I am therefore obliged to address myself to you to ask you to put an end to all these maneuvers, if you wish to avoid a fresh scandal—from which I shall certainly not retreat.

I have the honor to remain, Monsieur le Baron,
Your very humble and very obedient servant,
ALEXANDER PUSHKIN

iv

All night the snow had fallen, silently, ceaselessly. The pale, feeble sun that had just risen, staining the fog mauve, was already descending again toward the horizon, as if hurrying to escape from the boreal sky. The street sweepers, wearing felt boots, were raking the frozen pavement in front of the yellow palace. It was one o'clock in the afternoon.

Pushkin went out into the street, hailed a sleigh, and drove to the Café Wolff. (In St. Petersburg all the cafés were German, as all the restaurants were French.)

He sat down, ordered a lemonade, unfolded the paper. All around him women were chattering and eating the excellent Viennese pastries, served with a frothy crown of whipped cream.

He waited a long time. At four o'clock Danzas, once a fellow pupil at the lyceum, now a colonel of engineers, entered and came to his table. Danzas was a man who loved good living, good jokes, and a good laugh, a man so thoughtless of the future that at forty he was not married and had not established himself. Today he looked preoccupied. He held out a folded sheet of paper. Pushkin unfolded it and read:

Conditions of the duel between Monsieur le Baron George de Heeckeren and Monsieur Pushkin:

1. The two adversaries shall be placed at twenty paces distance, each at five paces from the two barriers, which shall be ten paces apart.

2. Each armed with a pistol, at a given signal they may advance toward each other—without, however, under any circumstances crossing the barrier—and make use of their weapons.

3. The witnesses of this affair, the undersigned, charged with full powers, guarantee upon their honor the strict execution of the above-mentioned conditions, each on his part.

January 27, 1837, at half past two in the afternoon.

Signed: COUNT D'ARCHIAC, *Attaché of the French Embassy*
CONSTANTINE DANZAS, *Lieutenant Colonel of Engineers*

"Good," said Pushkin. They left the café and mounted a sleigh. Danzas was silent. The sharp east wind raised a frozen dust that stung their eyes. Low, swollen clouds announced more snow. The morose tribe of officeholders, dressed in green, was leaving the ministries. Somewhere a bell sounded. The heavy boom-booms swelled out and fell like tears.

Danzas's heart sank. Everything was as usual, men were going about their business—and he was conveying perhaps to his death the first and the greatest poet brought forth by the soil of Russia.

Suddenly he had a moment of hope—a carriage was coming toward them; he recognized Natalya within. The cold had reddened her cheeks. Now she was turning her head, squinting her beautiful shortsighted eyes to read a sign. It was over. The carriage had passed. Pushkin had not seen his wife.

"Are you taking me to the fortress, by any chance?" he asked, seeing that their sleigh had taken the road to the Peter and Paul Fortress.

"No, we're almost there. And here is our adversary's carriage."

Little by little the street degenerated into a road. The wind blew stronger as night began to fall. On either hand fields of snow took the place of little woods of furry spruce. The two conveyances stopped. The seconds set out to find a suitable piece of ground. They walked slowly, their legs sinking knee-deep into the snow.

They stopped beside a glade that was surrounded by young firs. D'Archiac asked Pushkin if he thought the place suitable.

"It is all the same to me. Only try to get through with it quickly," he said, and sat down on a mound of snow.

In spite of his enormous coat, lined with bearskin, he felt the north wind blow colder and colder. The sky, over which the wind was driving low clouds, began to fill with shadows. The woods were turning black against the white snow. It seemed that there was nothing left in the world but those two colors and silence.

The two seconds had thrown their cloaks on the snow to mark the two barriers and were beginning to load the pistols.

"Aren't you ready yet?" he called to them. He was impatient to have it over. The preparation irked him. His fingers were numb with cold. At last Danzas called to him to come. He was placed five paces from the cloak that represented one of the barriers.

For the first time he raised his eyes and looked at the man opposite him. At last he had him under his pistol at twenty paces. How many times had he dreamed of slowly aiming at that pale forehead, on which Natasha's lips had perhaps lovingly rested. . . .

He looked at Danzas, as if to urge him to give the signal; saw him slowly lower his hat; and walked toward the barrier, raising his pistol. Suddenly he heard a shot; at the same time something struck him in the side, like the blow of a fist. The ground reared up, seemed to rise to meet him at a dizzy speed. He dropped into an abyss full of darkness and silence.

Pushkin had fallen on Danzas's cloak, with his head in the snow. The second ran toward him. Suddenly he recovered consciousness (it seemed to him that centuries had passed since he fell) and half raised himself, supporting himself on his left hand. An immense weariness filled him. His body was as heavy as lead.

"Wait," he said. "I feel strong enough to fire my shot."

Danzas put another pistol into his hand. (His own had fallen into the snow.) He aimed, pulled the trigger, saw his adversary drop to his knees. The world capsized again. His fingers let the weapon fall.

Danzas ran up. He raised his friend's beautiful head— with its closed eyes, with its curls spread over the fresh snow into which the wounded man's body had sunk. Pushkin half opened his eyes, drowned in darkness. Danzas bent to hear him:

"Is he dead?"

"No, but he is wounded in the arm and chest."

"It is strange," Pushkin murmured. "I had thought it would give me pleasure to kill him, but now I feel that it would not."

His body became heavier in Danzas's arms. Periods of unconsciousness alternated with moments of lucidity. The blood that flowed from his left side made a red pool in the snow; a vapor rose from it into the cold air.

D'Archiac went for the hackney carriage that was waiting in the road. The coachman helped him to dismantle the palisade that surrounded the dueling ground. The sleigh drew up beside the wounded man. Danzas lifted Pushkin up and laid him carefully within. His heart bled to find him as light as a woman. . . . How could such a slight, flexible body contain so much genius? He called to the coachman to drive at a walk.

Pushkin was suffering. A shooting pain ran through his left side. He pressed a handkerchief to his wound; when he removed it, it was sticky with blood. At every jolt nausea seized his throat.

Now it was completely dark. The sleigh moved quietly on. The horses' hoofs made a dull, regular sound on the snow. At six o'clock they drew up at Pushkin's door. Danzas went to call the servants. They came, terrified, bringing lamps.

Pushkin's valet took him in his arms and carried him as if he were a child.

"Does it make you sad to carry me like this?" the wounded man asked softly. The valet shook his head in silence.

Natasha was embroidering in the living room. She looked well and was elegantly dressed. Six years of St. Petersburg had refined her taste. She was now not only the most beautiful woman in Russia but also the best dressed. Alexandra, who was sitting beside her, looked like a pauper beside a queen.

Natalya was talking animatedly. She felt gay, almost happy. The D'Anthès incident appeared to be ended. For the last few days Alexander had seemed calmer, less excitable. There was no longer any talk of going to the country. Her life as a woman of fashion was beginning again. Who knows? she thought. Perhaps everything is going to turn out all right. . . .

Suddenly Danzas was announced. Danzas? What was he doing here at this hour? She hardly ever saw Danzas; he was an old friend of Alexander's. As he entered she gave him a look of terror, as if a presentiment of misfortune had touched her calm soul for the first time.

He explained in an embarrassed way that Alexander had fought a duel with Monsieur d'Anthès and had been wounded. . . . Oh! Slightly . . .

Natasha stood up, distraught. She saw neither Alexandra's sudden pallor nor the gesture that she made to repress her palpitating heart. She ran toward the door, pushing Danzas aside when he tried to stop her. Pushkin's valet appeared, carrying his inanimate master in his arms. Natasha raised her arms and fell without a sound at Danzas's feet.

"What do you think of my wound? At the time I felt a heavy blow in my side and a shooting pain in my back. On the way home I lost a good deal of blood."

"I cannot conceal from you that it is a serious wound."

"You can tell me the worst. Is it mortal?"

"It is my duty not to conceal it from you. However, let us wait until we hear the opinion of Dr. Arendt and Dr. Solomon, who will be here at any moment."

Pushkin lay on the narrow leather divan in his study. His eyes fell on his books, his faithful old companions, more faithful than men. He raised his hand to his damp forehead and closed his eyes.

"I thank you. You have dealt honestly with me. I must put my house in order."

The doctor bent over the divan.

"Do you wish to see any of your relatives or friends?"

"Then you think that I shall not last through the night?"

"Not at all. But I thought that it might give you pleasure to see them."

Pushkin turned his eyes to the wall. A sigh escaped from his bloodless lips.

"Farewell, friends. . . ."

It was impossible to determine whether these words were addressed to the world of men or to the world of books.

The doctors arrived. They were astonished to find the

patient so sad, so gentle, and so lucid. It had been long since anyone had seen Pushkin calm. It was as if all his bile had flowed out with his blood.

For him, everything was over. There remained the others —Natasha; Danzas, threatened with Siberia.

He said: "Do not give my wife too much hope. If it becomes known that she was calm at the moment of my death she will be accused of insensibility, she will be persecuted. . . ."

A few minutes later: "I ask the Czar to pardon Danzas. He is innocent. I caught him in the street and dragged him to the dueling grounds by force."

At times he forgot himself. His lips breathed inarticulate plaints. But when he sensed that his wife had entered or had even stopped outside the door, he woke.

"Don't let her come in. I do not want her to see me in this state. The poor thing—she suffers. But she is innocent!"

Natasha wandered from room to room like a soul in torment. Thoughts buzzed and collided in her head like flies. In a few hours dark circles had formed under her wide black eyes. She could not cry and did not know how to make herself useful. For the first time the unfortunate woman felt the weight of the immense responsibility that had been laid upon her. From thenceforth she would be the accursed woman who had cost Russia her first, her greatest poet.

At midnight the doctor of the imperial family brought a note from the Czar:

If it be God's pleasure that we shall not meet again in this world, I send you my pardon and counsel you to die a Christian. As to your wife and your children, do not concern yourself about them: I will take care of them. . . .

A priest was sent for. St. Petersburg was sleeping the heavy sleep of cities of stone. The house was full of stifled noises. Somewhere someone was whispering, doors were opened. Zhukovski, Vyazemski, Pletnev had come to take leave of the dying man.

All night Pushkin suffered. Toward dawn the pain became so fierce that even his fear of frightening his wife could not prevent him from crying out. Cold sweat covered his forehead, his arms grew icy up to the elbow. He cried:

"How long am I to be left to suffer like this? Quick, make an end! . . ."

Natasha was lying on a divan in the drawing room. Her black hair hung down to the floor, her distraught eyes passed unseeing across the faces that bent over her. At times a convulsive trembling shook her graceful limbs. She writhed on her narrow couch until her forehead touched her white knees. She had gritted her teeth so much that she had almost loosened them.

She did not hear the wounded man's terrible cries. About six o'clock she had fallen into a lethargic sleep and lay looking like a figure of stone in the gray light of dawn. His last cry aroused her. She sat up, haggard, thinking that she had been dreaming.

"It is nothing, Natasha, it was someone calling in the street," Princess Vyazemski said, bending over her; but as she spoke the words she wept.

At seven o'clock she was sent for. Alexander wished to take leave of his wife. She was led to his side. She fell on her knees beside his couch with a cry that sent a tear down Pushkin's pale cheek. Someone raised her; her disheveled hair hung down her back in two tresses like two long black snakes.

Pushkin beckoned to the doctor.

"Who is there?"

"Zhukovski and Vyazemski."

"Call them."

Zhukovski approached, with trembling lips, and took Pushkin's hand. It was already cold, but even in the sweat of his agony it remained an elegant and fastidious hand. He kissed it and moved away, to keep from bursting into tears. For Vyazemski the dying man had only a look and a movement of the hand. His strength was leaving him visibly. Pushkin was no longer of this world. Within himself he was mysteriously hearing death invade his limbs.

Suddenly he opened his eyes.

"Is Madame Karamzin there?"

The historian's widow, good, kind Catherine Andreevna —she to whom he had written a love letter when he was still at the lyceum—had become a good and faithful friend to him in the last ten years. She was now a beautiful old lady with white side curls. He had courted her daughters a little.

She arrived weeping and was led into the room. But she remained near the door, fearing to obtrude. Pushkin beckoned her to come nearer.

"Bless me," he said weakly. She made the sign of the Cross over him. Then he took her small hand, which had remained white and plump, and laid it on his forehead.

About noon a slight improvement could be seen. The opium was producing its effect. The patient was calmer. A little warmth returned to the cruelly torn body, from which life was withdrawing. His pulse, which had been imperceptible, began to throb again, feebly and irregularly.

The house filled. In the streets people met one another with the words, "Pushkin is dying!" The doors had to be closed. Unknown visitors climbed the stairs to inquire about the dying man's condition. For a moment the heart of Russia could be felt beating in the narrow antechamber that gave access to Pushkin's study.

In the evening the terrible dialogue with death began again. The patient was no longer tormented by pain but by a melancholy as piercing as physical suffering. Once again he saw his childhood in those cold, dilapidated Moscow houses; the lyceum, his youthful hopes; and then disillusionment, exile, the government's hatred. . . . He remembered Mrs. Kirchhof's prediction: "You will die young at the hands of a blond man."

How short his life had been! Yet what would he not have accomplished if he had been allowed to live! Now he must die at thirty-seven, without having fulfilled his destiny, without having seen Europe. He put his hands under his neck and murmured once more:

"Am I to be left . . . to suffer like this . . . long?"

The doctor bent over him. "You must suffer, my friend; there is nothing that can be done. But do not be ashamed of your suffering. Cry out, if it relieves you. . . ."

"No, I do not want to cry out. My wife . . . would be frightened. And then . . . I do not want to let the pain . . . be stronger than I am."

Pushkin's last day dawned in an icy fog. He lay unmoving on the leather divan, his eyes closed, so motionless and so pale that he seemed already dead.

But life was to reawaken spasmodically. At noon he opened his eyes and asked for a mirror. One was brought to him. He looked at himself and made a gesture of despair. Soon afterward he relapsed into a somnolence that was the forerunner of death.

At two o'clock (he had but three quarters of an hour to live) he asked for some whortleberry preserve, the sour taste of which he had always liked. It was sent for.

"Call my wife; let her feed me."

Natasha came in, tottering, and knelt at the dying man's bedside. Someone handed her the dish. She held the spoon to Pushkin's lips, then burst into tears and pressed her cheek against his damp forehead. He felt the warmth of her tears, once again he caressed her fine, silky hair, without opening his eyes.

"*Nichevo.* . . . It is better, thank God. . . . Go now."

She left the room, smiling through her tears.

"You will see—he will live. He will surely live!"

But he did not live.

His words were now only a breath, inaudible except to an ear held close to his lips. Once again he asked to be raised. Dr. Dahl took him under the arms and lifted him a little. Suddenly he opened his eyes, as if he were waking up.

"It is done," he said almost distinctly.

"Yes, it is done," the doctor answered, misunderstanding. "We have raised you."

"Life is done," the dying man repeated softly.

His breathing became slower. His arms grew cold to the shoulder, his legs to the knee. His right hand sketched one movement more, then fell back powerless upon the sheet. An expression of severe and majestic thought spread over the features so lately deformed by suffering.

Pushkin had ceased to live.

V

On February 4, 1837, two vehicles, preceded by a man on horseback, left St. Petersburg and took the road toward Pskov. Under his fur-lined cape the horseman wore the uniform of a police captain. He was escorting the carriage in which rode Mr. Turgenev, one of the Czar's gentlemen of the bedchamber.

A peasant's sledge, drawn by two horses that had difficulty in keeping up with Mr. Turgenev's well-fed *troika*, followed them at a distance, carrying a long black wooden box with leather handles.

The snowstorm that had been raging for three days had suddenly ceased. A big blue moon rose into a sky studded with stars, across which the Milky Way made a gray trail. On the road sleighs had already drawn interminable interlaced ribbons, which glittered in the moonlight. It was one of those cold, sparkling nights when the earth, under a blanket of fresh snow, seems uninhabited.

Mr. Turgenev thought sadly of all sorts of unpleasant things. A journey in company with a dead man, through a landscape that looked like the end of the world, predisposed him to melancholy.

Alexander Ivanovich Turgenev was a sentimentalist. He liked long, tender farewells, soulful poems, and handworked "keepsakes." All of which did not prevent him from appreciating good food, good wine, and pretty women. He was short and stout and fresh-complexioned, enjoyed doing a good turn, and was always running someone's errands.

His short figure was rendered invisible by the fur robes with which he had provided himself in view of the length of his journey. He looked out of the window of his berlin, yawned at the white landscape bordered on the horizon by a fringe of black firs, and ordered his coachman to drive faster. The sound of hoofs on the snow would have put him to sleep, had it not been for the thought of the dead man who was following him on the long peasant sledge.

He sighed, and remembered a verse from the Bible: "Vanity, vanity, all is vanity. . . ." The evening before, he had seen Pushkin nailed into that black box. Twenty-six years ago he had taken a little curly-haired boy—the nephew of his friend, the poet Vasili Lvovich Pushkin—to Tsarskoe Selo. Vasili Lvovich had been dead for five years; and today he himself was taking the body of Vasili Lvovich's nephew to the Svyatogorski Monastery, to the tomb of the Pushkins.

The sun of Russian poetry had set—who knew for how long? Perhaps forever! The state of Russian literature gave little occasion for hopes. It seemed destined to produce moralists, philosophers, mystics. . . . But poets?

Finally Alexander Ivanovich succeeded in falling asleep. When he woke the sun had transformed the landscape from gloom to gaiety. The berlin had left the dead man, with his wretched hired nags, far behind. Life was beginning again.

That evening Mr. Turgenev drank tea at the governor's house in Pskov and told the story of Pushkin's end to an audience of ladies in evening dress. The ladies shook their heads and sighed. Ah! Monsieur de Pushkin, what a loss, a perfect gentleman, and a great poet besides! Several of them remembered having known him at the time of his forced retirement in Mikhailovskoe, which was not very far away.

Mr. Turgenev fluttered about, babbled in French, and paid the ladies compliments. Indisputably some of the dead man's fame—the dead man who made a part of his baggage —was reflected upon himself.

At midnight the governor took him aside and showed him a letter that had just arrived from St. Petersburg. The obsequies of Kammerjunker Pushkin were to be marked by extreme simplicity, without any special honors, aside from those which were customary at the interment of a Russian gentleman. Such was His Majesty's will.

The authorities were excited. Even in death Pushkin still gave them trouble. He had always been a railer, a dangerous man, whose latent hostility might at any moment be expected to break out. Now it appeared that he was the leader of a widespread opposition. . . .

For two days people in St. Petersburg had met one another with the question, "Have you any news of Pushkin? How is he?" When he died the little apartment on Moika Quay was stormed by such a crowd that the doors had to be shut to keep people from being crushed to death. An unheard-of thing! This gentleman was mourned by the common people! The court and the reigning beauties pitied the poor Heeckerens—degraded, disgraced, and forced to leave the country. . . . But, below them, Russia wept for her first love. . . .

The papers devoted long articles to him. Fortunately the authorities were on hand to call the journalists to order: Was the deceased a general or a statesman, to justify this indecent display of regret? The censorship forbade even the mention of Pushkin's name.

But his corpse was as dangerous as a flag. As long as it was there, trouble was to be feared. . . . Was it not rumored that the rabble were talking of smashing the windows of the Dutch embassy? That his obsequies would be made an excuse for demonstrations? That it would be General Lamarque's funeral all over again? It was subversion, a riot, an absolute revolt! And this was how the Czar's goodness was rewarded—the Czar, who had showered kindnesses upon Pushkin's widow. . . . Oh, what an ungrateful lot the people were!

At all costs the body must be got rid of. It was removed by night and transported to a different church from the one originally designated, to throw the "rioters" off the track. This nocturnal transfer of the remains was attended by more police and plain-clothes men than members of the family and friends.

The religious service was hurriedly dispatched. The priest, only half awake, swallowed the words. Faster, faster! The police were waiting for the subversive dead man. At last the coffin could be loaded onto the sledge; and it set off, followed by Mr. Turgenev and a police officer, who were ordered to accompany it to the province of Pskov.

But there might still be trouble. What if the province should show signs of rebellion too? An order was sent to the governor of Pskov, forbidding any manifestations, even of a religious nature, "except such as were customary at the interment of a Russian gentleman."

Kindhearted Mr. Turgenev was saddened by the order. The dead man's disgrace—like his fame—fell partly on him.

The next morning, sobered and chilly, he continued his journey; in spite of himself he could not help hearing the tired trot of the two nags that were drawing the coffin. At three o'clock they arrived at a long, low house. An old woman and a girl came to meet them. It was Trigorskoe, aging and empty. Zizi, who had married, lived far away. She was no longer the young girl whose waist was slimmer than the stem of a champagné glass, but a fat woman, eternally pregnant. Annie, who had remained an old maid, lived in St. Petersburg. Of all the young people, only little Masha was left—she to whom Pushkin had taught grammar. Now she was eighteen, and people called her Maria Ivanovna.

Mr. Turgenev kissed Mrs. Ossipov's hand; but she touched his forehead with her lips, according to the old Russian custom. She was now an old woman who wore outmoded bonnets and no longer tried to look younger than her years. The news of Pushkin's death had already reached her.

They entered. A fire crackled on the hearth, at which Alexander had so often read poems to an attentive circle of young ladies. Mrs. Ossipov poured tea and displayed albums that contained poems and drawings by Pushkin. But Mr. Turgenev was inattentive. He looked at Masha. She was dark-haired and charming, with surprised blue eyes and a tender smile. He told the story of Pushkin's end again. He felt contented, dreamy, almost in love.

At seven o'clock the dead man arrived, jouncing on the sledge behind the two exhausted nags. They had almost forgotten him.

The burial was to take place the following morning at six o'clock. Mr. Turgenev took leave of Trigorskoe and its two mistresses almost tenderly. He promised to come back and to send them his portrait. In fact he had almost made up his mind to do so. Mrs. Ossipov presented him with a hand-worked souvenir and kissed him on the forehead again. He went to the monastery. The police officer followed him sulkily. He had two nights' sleep to make up.

Peasants were already digging the grave. In spite of the cold, they were sweating. The frozen earth was difficult to dig. When they saw the barin they took off their caps.

Finally the grave was ready. The peasants brought up the coffin on their shoulders and lowered it into the grave. Mr. Turgenev threw in a handful of earth and started to say a few well-chosen words, but remembered that there was no one present except a few illiterate muzhiks and a policeman and thought better of it. The frozen earth dropped onto the coffin with a faint, dry sound that was somehow definitive.

Mr. Turgenev was in a hurry to get back. It was cold, and the low clouds promised a new snowstorm. Finally the grave was filled. He tipped the gravediggers and left with his policeman. The peasants picked up their tools and went away too. Snow began to fall. Little by little it covered the new grave, upon which stood a temporary cross of unpainted wood.

vi

During the winter of 1865 a rich and influential gentleman, Baron George d'Anthès de Heeckeren, arrived in Nice to spend a few weeks far from Paris and its rains, which caused him painful seizures of the gout. The cold, dry climate of Alsatia was better for his health. He had had the family manor house—vast and uncomfortable, and built of pink Vosges stone—put in livable condition and had even had gas laid on; but the old house called up too many sad memories, such as the death of his wife at the birth of their fourth child.

Catherine, for whom he had sent to Russia after he had himself reached France in a headlong journey, had lived thenceforth in perpetual adoration of the husband who had dropped out of the sky for her. At the desire of her new family she had adopted the Roman Catholic faith. He remembered her as a gentle and submissive woman. After her death he had not remarried.

Now he was old and respected, one of the founders of the Paris Gas Company, which had been making remarkable strides in the last few years. He had continued to join the name of his father-by-adoption to his own name, out of gratitude for the Dutch diplomat's care for him, which had never failed. Now the old Baron van Heeckeren was his country's ambassador in Vienna, where he filled his post with the same skill and the same lack of scruples that had won him the hatred and the esteem of St. Petersburg. He was still a passionate collector of paintings and antiques.

Baron d'Anthès's fortune now allowed him to cherish political ambitions of his own. He dreamed of a seat in the Senate. For thirteen years Napoleon's nephew had reigned over France. At first he had been popular, with his beautiful Spanish empress, but ever since the beginning of the ill-starred Mexican adventure the stubborn, stone-ridden Emperor's prestige had been steadily going down. Eugénie's influence was fatal to him. Satirical songs were sung about them in Paris. On the other hand, the idea of the restoration of the Comte de Paris was popular among both the upper and lower middle classes. As it happened, Baron d'Anthès's personal preferences and family traditions both inclined him toward royalist ideas.

He thought of all these things as he walked slowly along the promenade, enjoying the blue sky and the warm sun. Five years earlier France had recovered Nice and this bit of flowery coast, beautiful with an almost too conventional beauty. The English and the Russians came there by thousands. Hotels were hurriedly built, palms planted along the tideless sea, which was as blue as a basin of indigo and barely ruffled by the wind.

At fifty-three, the baron still had manifest traces of his former distinguished bearing. He stood straight, he had no unnecessary fat, his profile was Greek. His hair, which was turning white, was still thick and wavy. He wore a pointed beard, in the Spanish style which had been brought into fashion by Napoleon III.

Even now, women turned round as he passed, in spite of his slow, gouty walk and the bags under his eyes due to kidney trouble. Women still interested him. He looked at those who passed him on the promenade with the eyes of a man who has not abdicated. However, few of them were worth noticing: Englishwomen with horse faces, wearing short skirts that revealed striped cotton pantalettes.

Suddenly the baron started. A lady of some fifty years, still beautiful in spite of the gray tresses that framed the pure oval of her face and her wide black eyes, had almost touched him as she passed.

Could it be possible? Natalya, Natalya here? He turned

and would have hurried after her, but she was already some distance away, walking with her face turned toward the sea, gazing at it with that familiar, calm expression. Obviously she had not noticed the old, bearded man, and besides, would she have recognized him, would she have permitted him to speak to her? Since the catastrophe she had never written to the D'Anthèses. And Catherine, who was always jealous, had preferred to let the memory of her too beautiful sister fade away.

In Baron d'Anthès's mind memories rose tumultuously. Natasha's image, which twenty-seven years of apparent forgetfulness had not succeeded in tarnishing, returned to the surface: Natasha in a rose-pink ball dress, an ostrich plume softly caressing the charming contour of her head and following the hollow of her bare shoulder. Natasha, in a riding habit, galloping beside him to the St. Petersburg Islands, Natasha weeping, wringing her hands, imploring him to let her go, at the rendezvous arranged by Idalya Poletika . . .

Then his marriage to Catherine, and two months later the duel with Pushkin. God was his witness, he had not wished the death of his rival. His hand, which was aiming at his adversary's legs, had swerved. But that had not prevented the explosion of a nation's indignation, the madness that had seized Russia on the news of Pushkin's death.

He recollected those last days in St. Petersburg, the siege that the baron, Catherine, and he had been forced to undergo at the Dutch embassy. Then his degradation, his journey in a sleigh, his wounded arm, the sling, the jolting.

It was his whole youth that had passed by him in the person of that woman whose full skirt had almost touched him. He went in—agitated, aged as it were, by the recollection of that tragic past.

She who had so violently aroused George d'Anthès's memories continued her walk toward the hotel at which she was staying under the name of Mrs. Lanskoi. It was twenty years since she had ceased to call herself Natalya Pushkin. At that time seven years had passed since her first husband's death.

At first her grief and her repentance had been so great that her reason had been feared for. She was unable to attend the funeral, and it was not until two years later that she went to the Svyatogorski Monastery to perform her last duty to "poor Pushkin." She found the grave well looked after and provided with flowers by the attentive care of Mrs. Ossipov, but when she went to thank the old lady the latter gave her such an icy reception that she never risked another visit to Trigorskoe.

To Pushkin's friends—she knew—she had never been a wife and a widow worthy of him. And yet she had observed her period of mourning decently and strictly, she had retired for two years to the Linen Factories, her brother's estate, which he had inherited from the Goncharovs. Life was not gay there, especially after her triumphs in St. Petersburg—between Alexandra, who was as stricken as a real widow, and a sister-in-law who was always in a huff over the elegant ladies who came from St. Petersburg to visit Natalya.

Pushkin's four children grew up there. Little by little the tragic memories grew dim. One day they simply went back to St. Petersburg—perfectly quietly, of course—Alexandra, the children, and herself.

St. Petersburg was agog over the Eastern question and had entirely forgotten Pushkin's death. To the world in general Natalya was simply the widow of a gentleman of the bedchamber who had been killed in a duel. She lived in retirement, always a little mournful, a little ill.

December 1841 . . . Christmas Eve. There was a fine dry cold. St. Petersburg was a forest of young firs, waiting for buyers. The shops were lighted up by three o'clock in the afternoon.

A luxurious vehicle drew up before a big toy store. Policemen blocked off a passage across the sidewalk. The double doors, decorated with the imperial eagles, opened to let out a tall man. It was the Emperor Nicholas Pavlovich. He was almost fifty, his hair was gray, but he still held himself straight and his look was commanding. He was the inflexible Autocrat of All the Russias, the mainstay of European reaction, the human buttress whose thrust prevented the monarchical principle from collapsing in a Europe sapped by the ideas of '89.

He had come in person to choose Christmas presents for the heir to the throne, his sisters, and his cousins. The owner of the shop, arriving in hot haste, had the latest novelties unpacked. Suddenly the Emperor's eyes fell on a young woman who had been in the shop choosing toys at the time of his arrival and who waited, sunk in a deep curtsy.

That figure, those black eyes, and, under her widow's bonnet, those shining curls . . . Natalya, Natalya Pushkin? . . . The Czar stepped toward her, joyful, almost agitated. Natalya in St. Petersburg? But she must return to the Anichkov Palace, come to the balls, as before. . . . The court could not be deprived of such an ornament! She returned. The first function she attended was a costume ball. Natalya wore Turkish slippers and long trousers. The silky veils of her "Hebrew" costume fluttered around her, swathed her from head to waist. She had lost none of her beauty. Her years of being forgotten had, as it were, renewed her.

The Emperor, conquered, had taken her by the hand and led her up to the Empress. The latter raised her lorgnette to her eyes.

"Charming! Absolutely ravishing!" she said.

Life in the great world, the life she loved so well, began for her again. Now she was a widow and free; no one followed her jealously when she went to a ball; no figure stood before her like a remorse, black against the pedestal of a column in some festive hall. Only Alexandra's eyes sometimes reproached her for her forgetfulness, her posthumous infidelity.

Little by little the idea of marrying again developed in her small bird brain. She was loved by the Czar, whose constant kindness to her had not failed to attract attention. She began to be courted. Paul Lanskoi, Idalya's lover, the very man who had mounted guard under the window on the day of her first and only rendezvous with George d'Anthès, showed himself particularly attentive.

She was rumored to be the Czar's mistress. . . . But, bah! Even if it were true, the Emperor's leavings were still good enough for a captain in the Horse Guards!

Their union was as calm as her first union had been tragic and stormy. For Lanskoi she was the beginning of a dizzyingly rapid rise. He quickly became a colonel, then a general. Their first child, a girl, had the Emperor for godfather.

The Czar went to the family parties General Lanskoi

gave for his officers, talked familiarly to the general's charming wife, then he would go upstairs to the nursery and spend
a long time contemplating his goddaughter. Evil tongues
said that she was much more closely related to him.

Now Natalya was a widow for the second time. Lanskoi
was no more. And for ten years the man who had played so
great a role in her life, Czar Nicholas, had been dead too,
killed by the Russian Army's reverses in the Crimean War.

She remembered the last time that she had seen the Czar.
The evening before, he had expired on his little camp bed.
He had been dressed and rouged, and he lay on the cata-
falque—so tall and so heavy in his green general's uniform
that he gave the impression of being his own statue.

The Emperor's personal valet had brought General Lanskoi's widow a little medallion which the late Emperor had
worn around his neck and in which there was a portrait of
Natalya Pushkin in a ball gown and two locks of hair, one
dark, the other blond. The blond lock was the Empress's.

She had prayed for a long time at the foot of the cata-
falque, then she had gone away, beautiful in her mourning
dress, which swept the parquet floors of the imperial palace
with an autumnal sound.

She never returned to the palace. The new Emperor,
Alexander II, was young and in love with new ideas, as his
uncle, Alexander I, had once been. He reorganized the
army, the civil service, the judiciary, founded universities,
wanted to emancipate the peasants. . . . This new Russia
of the sixties was no longer the country she had known. She
belonged to the past. Her life had come to an end with the
death of Nicholas. She had been a part of his reign. More

and more she became a forgotten woman, triply widowed. . . .

Pushkin's four children had left her. Lanskoi was dead. Alexandra, who late in life had become Baroness Friesenhoff, had left her too. Natalya wandered through a huge, empty house, full of old furniture and old memories, a lady in black who had been beautiful. To an observer her life suggested the movements of a beautiful fish imprisoned in a globe.

But while she, and all those for whom she had lived, slowly returned to nothingness, the other, the dead man of Svyatogorsk, became ever more alive, more radiant, more present.

He remained the Unique. He had no disciples, but he had believers. Russian letters, which by a single effort he had raised to the level of a world literature, were prospering magnificently and strangely, with Tolstoi, Dostoevski, Turgenev. With them, Russian literature had become profound, shadowy, painful, moralizing.

Their Russia had no frontier except with God. It was a land of madmen, of seers, of drunkards, of criminals, and of idiots, who bore all humanity's sins and all its hopes. And in the depths of their gehenna Russia's writers warmed themselves at the sun of Pushkin, who had been so simple and so human.

He had known how to live and to create, in spite of evil. And since his death Russian writers, tortured by the evil that they could not accept, sought painfully for his secret.

But he remained the Unequaled, beloved of women and musicians. He was the cornerstone and the keystone of Russian literature. And in spite of his apotheosis, he remained living and accessible to all, as he had predicted in the majestic poem that he wrote in his last days, under a foreboding of death, like an organ point upon an unfinished work. . . .

Exegi Monumentum

Unto myself I reared a monument not builded
By hands; a track thereto the people's feet will tread;
Not Alexander's shaft is lofty as my pillar
*   That proudly lifts its splendid head.*

Not wholly shall I die—but in the lyre my spirit
Shall, incorruptible and bodiless, survive—
And I shall know renown as long as under heaven
*   One poet yet remains alive.*

The rumor of my fame will sweep through vasty Russia,
And all its peoples speak this name, whose light shall reign
Alike for haughty Slav, and Finn, and savage Tungus,
*   And Kalmuck riders of the plain.*

I shall be loved, and long the people will remember
The kindly thoughts I stirred—my music's brightest crown,
How in this cruel age I celebrated freedom,
*   And begged for ruth toward those cast down.*

Oh, Muse, as ever, now obey your God's commandments,
Of insult unafraid, to praise and slander cool,
Demanding no reward, sing on, but in your wisdom
*   Be silent when you meet a fool.*[1]

[1]From *The Poems, Prose and Plays of Alexander Pushkin*, Copyright, 1936, by Random House, Inc.